Today's health service

-a user's guide-

Robert Eagle

CHANNEL FOUR TELEVISION

CONTENTS

INTRODUCTION
WHAT HAS HAPPENED
TO THE NHS?

The past few years have seen more upheaval in Britain's National Health Service than at any time since it was set up almost 50 years ago. The changes have split the medical profession and caused uproar in Parliament. But the public is left confused by what is going on.

Some of the issues – such as waiting lists – seem easy enough to grasp. But what of the many other buzzwords such as 'NHS trusts', 'fundholders', the 'internal market'? What do these mean to the patient waiting for an operation or looking for a GP? How might *your* treatment be affected?

Critics of the changes have claimed that they have been introduced too quickly and that some patients will benefit at the expense of others. There have certainly been teething troubles.

On the other hand, there has been a lot of effort to encourage hospitals and GPs to raise their standards. Patients are being offered information – once very hard to obtain – about the standards of service they can expect. More than that, they are actually being encouraged to comment and complain if the service does not meet their needs. A *Patient's Charter* outlining what people can expect of the health service *by right* was drawn up by the Department of Health in 1991. This was extended in 1993 to spell out what people are entitled to expect from their GPs.

THE PATIENT'S CHARTER – CONSUMER RIGHTS OR PUBLIC RELATIONS?

Some of the ten rights delineated in the *Charter* were backed by existing laws; others were just statements of government policy – admirable, perhaps, but not enforceable in the courts. However, they did give an idea of what the government was trying to achieve. Those ten rights are the subject of the next ten chapters of this book.

So how will patients gain, and how might they lose, from the NHS reforms? Are the rights laid down in the *Patient's Charter* just politicians' promises? To what extent are they guaranteed by law?

Taking the *Patient's Charter* as a framework, this book examines how the NHS actually works. It suggests how patients can get the best from the health service and what they can do if the best is not forthcoming.

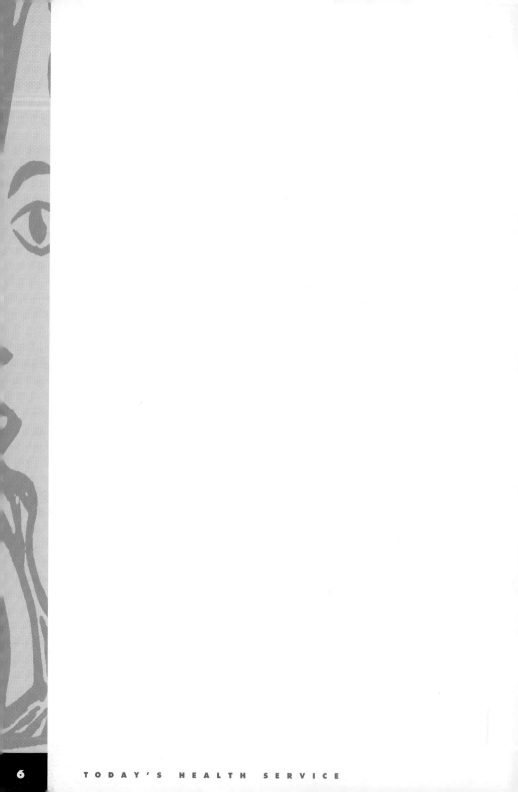

1

CARE BASED ON NEED

The right to receive health care on the basis of clinical need, regardless of ability to pay

The founding of the National Health Service in 1948 was undoubtedly one of the boldest, most imaginative and altruistic political projects this country has ever seen. The concept that medical treatment should be freely available for all was truly revolutionary.

Many doctors hated the idea. They feared that their professional status would be compromised, that they would become minions of a state service which would seek to control their every action.

How things have changed! When, 40 years later, a radical government (right-wing Conservative this time, not Labour left) decided that the NHS needed reform, the British Medical Association (BMA) was appalled. Despite its many faults, the vast majority of doctors were now very comfortable with this state service and determined that it should not be compromised.

But while doctors and government now seemed to be fighting from different corners, everyone acknowledged that the NHS faced severe difficulties. The basic problem was cost. Despite their bold vision, the founders of the NHS had suffered from a delusion: they believed that, when medicine became freely available, the population would become healthier and demand for treatment would fall away. In fact, the opposite has proved to be the case. The advances of medical science have meant that more and more conditions, once incurable, can now be relieved. New technology has brought new standards of care. All these innovations have come at a price, but because everyone has the right to be treated, demand for these costly services has soared. People are also living longer, and an older population has greater need for medical care.

This has been, of course, a universal problem. Health costs have risen all over the world for the same reasons. In 1992, Britain was spending on the NHS about £640 per year per head of population, a total budget of about £36 billion. But this was much less than other developed countries. We still spend only two thirds of what the French devote from their national income on health, and just over half what the Americans spend.

Successive governments, alarmed by the prospect of having to raise taxes endlessly to cope with demand, were tight with funds. To some extent, costs could be kept down by paying doctors and nurses less than they would earn elsewhere. (With a total staff of nearly one million people, the NHS was Europe's biggest employer, second only to the Red Army!) The other way of keeping costs down was by rationing care: waiting lists for operations flourished. If you were an elderly patient needing a hip replacement (a good example of the new treatments devised since 1948), you might well die before your turn came round.

So how could the demand for treatment be satisfied without leting costs rise or standards fall? The answer which government came up with in the late 1980s was to try to improve efficiency, by changing the way the NHS was run.

'PURCHASERS' AND 'PROVIDERS'

The most radical change was to create what was called an 'internal market' by splitting the service into 'purchasers' and 'providers'. The internal market was a way of making the NHS work more like private industry, where competition is supposed to keep prices low and quality high. In this market place of medical care, purchasers were those who bought treatments for patients; providers were those who provided them. District health authorities were the main purchasers, while hospitals and GPs were the principal providers.

The idea was that purchasers should buy, and providers should provide, the best quality care at the most competitive prices. If Hospital X could perform an operation for £400, it would get more business than Hospital Y, which charged £500. If their prices were similar, the hospital with shorter waiting lists, or which offered some other quality advantage, would have the edge.

Until 1991, health authorities had been responsible for running the hospitals in their districts. Now the authorities were slimmed down, and hospitals took on their own day-to-day management. Health authorities still had a broad responsibility to ensure that hospitals in their district could provide the range of care needed by the local population as a whole. But apart from that, their main job was to make annual contracts with hospitals, agreeing in advance the services the hospital would provide and the price to be paid for them. Some hospitals were encouraged to become totally independent of their district health authority by becoming 'NHS trusts'. (For a diagram of NHS organisation, see p.100.)

Meanwhile, family health services authorities (previously known as family practitioner committees) were the purchasers who made contracts with the providers of non-hospital care: general practitioners, dentists, pharmacists and opticians.

General practitioners working in larger practices were offered the opportunity of becoming purchasers as well as providers. If a practice had more than 11,000 patients (this was later reduced to 7000), the doctors could apply to become 'fundholders'. They would be given their own budget to purchase drugs and hospital care for their patients. Like district health authorities, fundholding GPs could make their own contracts with hospitals and decide themselves where to have their patients treated.

PREVENTION AS WELL AS CURE

In 1990, the government drew up new contracts for GPs and dentists which were intended to encourage them to do more work to prevent disease. GPs were expected to provide health checks for patients; they also received special payments for immunising and screening and for running health promotion clinics. These payments were not extra income for GPs: the money was found by reducing other fees and allowances they had been entitled to.

Dentists, instead of being paid for each treatment, were to be paid a single annual fee for each child on their list. And there were incentives for quality rather than quantity: if fillings fell out within a year, they had to be replaced free of charge.

CARE OF OLD AND DISABLED PEOPLE

Another big change was to be in the way government paid for residential care for old and mentally or physically disabled people. Between 1979 and 1989, the cost to the state of residential care had risen 100-fold, from £10 million to £1 billion. The main reason for this was that the Department of Social Security had to pay for the accommodation of anyone who was entitled to Income Support, and the majority of people in residential care fell into this category. With an ever-increasing elderly population, these costs were obviously going to keep on growing.

Moreover, people who looked after their own relatives at home had long complained that they got very little financial or practical help. The system encouraged carers to put relatives into residential care as soon as they became a burden.

The government's response was to put the purchasing of residential care into the hands of local authorities – a programme known as 'Care in the Community'. The DSS would no longer be expected to pay whatever fees residential homes cared to charge. Money would go to councils, who would have to work with the local health authorities to decide who should be looked after in residential homes, who needed medical support and who should be looked after at home (by their family or other carers) and what should be paid for these various services.

CHANGED FOR BETTER - OR FOR WORSE?

Criticisms of the changes came from all quarters and did not follow conventional party political lines. The main line of attack was that competition did not necessarily guarantee better quality: providers might be encouraged to cut corners to keep prices down, or might be forced to close down if their high standards obliged them to charge high prices. There was widespread concern that a 'two-tier' system would develop, with well-funded purchasers being able to secure better service for their patients. There was mistrust of the new NHS trusts because they were less accountable to the public than health authorities. Fundholding aroused suspicion because it was thought that GPs would be tempted to base their treatment decisions on cost rather than medical need. And even though the changes in residential care were to be introduced over a three-year period, beginning in 1993, local authorities were ill-prepared for their new role. Indeed there were fears that all these changes were being introduced too quickly and with too little planning.

All radical changes cause dismay and confusion, and a lot of dust still has to settle. Despite early misgivings about NHS trusts and fundholding, more and more hospitals and GP practices are opting for the independence these arrangements confer.

However, NHS dental services have become difficult to obtain in some parts of the country as a result of dentists' dissatisfaction with the new rates of pay offered by the Department of Health. In 1991, their new contracts had encouraged them to take on more patients – and earn more money – than the Department of Health had expected. So the following year the DoH reduced the amount it paid them by 7 per cent. Not surprisingly, this caused resentment. A British Dental Association survey in late 1992 found that many dentists were no longer taking on new NHS patients.

In addition, NHS prescription charges have risen to a level that makes many commonly prescribed medicines cheaper to buy directly over the counter from the pharmacist.

Hospital treatment, too, has been adversely affected in some areas. Some health authorities have now withdrawn from providing treatments which may not be medically urgent, but which may mean a great deal to people's well-being. *In vitro* fertilisation, reversal of sterilisation, varicose vein operations, cosmetic surgery such as breast reduction or tattoo removal – all these may be difficult, perhaps impossible, to obtain on the NHS in some places. In many areas, waiting lists have been 'recycled' so that they disappear from official figures but emerge in other ways. And the problems of mental health have barely been addressed by the changes. A quarter of all NHS in-patients are receiving psychiatric care, but only half of these actually need to be kept in hospital; they remain there because there is nowhere else for them to go. Those who are discharged into 'community care' are often left to fend for themselves.

The new GP contracts may have pressurised lazy doctors to do a better job, but the more conscientious felt insulted. Almost all of them resented the extra paperwork. There was also concern that the money spent on health promotion was not reaching the more deprived sections of the community who suffer the worst health.

Nevertheless many have been enthused by the changes. In the words of an eminent medical professor who is deputy chairman of one of the first NHS hospital trusts:

There are certainly things to criticise, but the idea of self-management is not one of them. It is clearly better to budget our own money than have it budgeted for us – savings made in one area can be spent on other things, which was often impossible under the old system. This is why we have been able to treat more patients despite an income that has been cut in real terms.

More work for less money: that is the unappetising thistle the health service now has to chew on. And the fact remains that there is not enough money in the health budget to treat everyone on the basis of clinical need. At best, they are treated on the basis of comparative need.

GENERAL PRACTITIONERS

The right to be registered with a general practitioner

Being registered with a GP is not just a right for NHS patients, it is a necessity. The general practitioner is the gatekeeper to almost all NHS services. A poor GP can stand in the way of your getting appropriate treatment when you need it. A good one will cherish you and should be cherished in return!

WHAT DOES A GP DO?

General practitioners deal with the great majority of complaints for which patients seek treatment. If you do need specialist treatment, it is your GP who has to refer you. If you are disabled, elderly, mentally ill or mentally handicapped, your GP can play an important part in ensuring you get the social services support and benefits to which you may be entitled. You do not have to be registered with a GP to get emergency treatment, but you will have difficulty getting regular health care on the NHS if you are not.

As far as treatment is concerned, GPs used to confine themselves largely to prescribing medicines and/or offering advice. However, more and more of them now have the qualifications and interest to offer more specialist services, such as contraception, antenatal and obstetric care and minor surgical procedures. GPs are also paid to provide basic check-ups and screening services, such as testing for high blood pressure, diabetes and cervical cancer, and for encouraging parents to bring in their children for immunisation against infectious diseases such as polio, diphtheria, whooping cough, measles, rubella (German measles) and mumps. Every new patient who joins a GP's list should be offered a basic health check within 28 days. All patients are entitled to a check every three years if they have not seen their GP for any other reason, and patients over 75 years old are entitled to a check every year. (The doctor may carry out these checks personally, but many will pass you on to their practice nurses for most routine ones.) Your GP is obliged to offer these checks, but they are not compulsory for patients: if you do not think them necessary, you don't have to accept them.

The kind of service you get from a GP can vary enormously, depending on the individual doctor. Most GPs now have appointments systems at their surgeries, though some still operate on a 'first come, first served' basis. There are also considerable differences in their willingness to visit you at home, especially at night. GPs also differ in their style of practice. Some are very brisk, while others like to spend time listening to their patients. Some prefer to explain in great detail why they are offering a particular treatment, while others seem to have a more 'doctor knows best' approach.

A great deal of the work done by a conscientious GP is not confined to diagnosis and treatment. Many GPs spend a lot of time on problems which are social rather than strictly medical, especially if they have patients who are old, hard up or disadvantaged. This is justified, for people who are poor tend to have worse health and lower life expectancy than the better-off.

HOW GPs WORK

The traditional picture of GPs as independent practitioners ministering single-handed to their patients is not completely a thing of the past, but it is far from typical. Today, only 10 per cent of GPs are in practice by themselves. The great majority now work with other GPs in group practices, pooling their income and sharing expenses, and many have their surgeries in health centres which may house several practices.

In the current jargon, the GP is the key member of the 'primary health care team', which will generally include a practice nurse, health visitors, district nurses, a psychiatric nurse, chiropodist, speech therapist and other health professionals. In a large health centre, all members of this team will work under the same roof. Whether they actually operate as a 'team' will largely depend on the individuals involved. Larger practices may have several receptionists and a practice manager who organises appointments, clinics and much of the team's other day-to-day business.

Even though most GPs do not work single-handed, they have retained much of their traditional independence. Unlike NHS hospital doctors, GPs are not salaried employees: they are self-employed and provide their services under a contract with their local family health services authority (FHSA). While this does not mean that GPs are completely free agents who can practise entirely at will, their self-employed status is jealously guarded by the British Medical Association, which represents doctors' interests.

There are tax advantages in being self-employed, but this is not the only reason why GPs like their independence. As independent contractors, GPs can chose whether or not to offer certain services, such as advising on and supplying contraception; they are also free to prescribe medicines and treat patients as they see fit and to select the doctors to whom they refer their patients for specialist care (*see* Chapter 4 on consultants).

GPs earn most of their income from the number of patients on their list. They are paid a fee for each patient, ranging from £14.30 a year for patients under 65 to £36.45 for those over 75. The rest of their income comes from fees for certain services such as contraception and night calls, from allowances towards the cost of their staff and premises, and from target payments for vaccinations and cervical smear tests.

Target payments are now an important part of every GP's income. If GPs can show that they have carried out 90 per cent of the recommended immunisation procedures for children on their list under two years old, they can earn a target fee of £1860. If they have regularly provided smear tests for more than 80 per cent of their female patients in the 25–64 age group, they can earn a fee of £2280. These fees are obviously a powerful incentive for doctors to do this kind of preventive medicine.

However, they can sometimes cause friction between doctor and patient, for if the doctor falls short of these targets by even 1 per cent, the fees fall dramatically. For instance, doctors who only manage to do 89 per cent of the target figure for immunisations receive just £620 instead of £1860. There have been cases where GPs have struck patients off their list for refusing to have smears or let their children be immunised.

Some health groups have campaigned for a salaried GP service. One of the main arguments for this is that GPs could then be obliged to offer the services most needed in the area where they practise. In inner city areas such as central London, for instance, quite a high proportion of GPs work single-handed and, even if they want to, cannot offer as wide a range of services as a group practice. Opponents of a salaried service argue that GPs already have financial inducements to provide these services for their patients and are best placed to decide what they should offer.

The independent status of GPs has considerable bearing on your rights as a patient. For example, although you have the right to be registered with a GP, this does not mean that you can necessarily be registered with the GP you want. GPs can refuse to take you on their list – or can take you off it – without giving any reason. In practice, they usually have no objection to taking on new patients, as they earn a capitation fee for everyone on their list. The usual reason for refusing to take on a new patient is that the practice list is full. The average GP's list comprises about 2000 patients; adding more to the list may mean more money for the doctor, but it can also mean more work. Elderly patients, for instance, usually need more medical attention than young adults – and more than is covered by the extra fees that GPs can claim for the over-75s on their list. An overcrowded surgery also means less time for each patient.

Occasionally, however, the 'full list' may be used as an excuse not to take on a patient who might be regarded as troublesome or too much work. Sadly, this category sometimes includes homeless people, patients who have fallen out with other doctors and patients with complaints which are likely to call for more than the average amount of care and attention.

Another reason for refusing to take a patient on is that they live outside the practice 'catchment area'. In fact, practices do not have to have strictly defined boundaries. The reason is more likely to be that the doctor does not want to have to travel a long way if a home visit is necessary.

Just as GPs have a right to refuse to take you on to their list, they can also turf you off it at any time without giving a reason. You have a similar right: you can leave your GP and register with another, also without asking permission or giving a reason. However, it is not always easy to find another conveniently located GP, especially if you live in a country area. If you cannot find a GP, the local family health services authority is obliged to find one for you. That GP then has to accept you as a patient for at least three months. If you get yourself a reputation for being a 'difficult' patient, you could find yourself on a merry-go-round, being switched from one doctor to another four times a year.

If you are registered with a GP in a group practice, you do not have an automatic right to be seen and treated by that particular doctor. Indeed, if you do join a practice list, it is quite possible that you will find yourself registered with a different GP from the one whose list you applied to join. This is usually nothing to worry about. If you can wait for an appointment, you should be able to be seen by the doctor of your choice.

CHOOSING A GP

The traditional way of finding a good GP is by word of mouth, by asking friends and neighbours. This is usually adequate as long as you take the trouble to ask a number of patients of different doctors and make allowance for personal bias.

However, you will probably get more factual information from the local directory of GPs, which should be available at your post office, library, citizen's advice bureau and/or community health council or direct from your local FHSA, whose job it is to draw up such a local directory. (In Scotland, the health boards compile these lists; in Northern Ireland, it is the health and social services board.) These local directories provide most of what you need to know about the services offered by GPs.

As of April 1993, new Charter Standards laid down by the Department of Health oblige FHSAs to act promptly and efficiently to help patients find a GP. If you are not already registered with a

GP, the FHSA should find you one within two working days. If you want to change doctors, you should be sent details of how to change, together with a list of local doctors, also within two working days.

If you are not in a tearing hurry to find a doctor, it is worthwhile hunting around for a practice which suits your needs. GP practices have to publish their own leaflets describing the doctors and their services. It is up to the doctors themselves where they make these leaflets available, but you should at least be able to get one at the practice itself. In fact, it is a good idea to visit the surgery to get a feel for a practice. If you have young children, for instance, take a look round to see if there are toys and children's books in the waiting room, which would suggest that the doctors are sympathetic to young patients. And talk to the receptionist: is she friendly and helpful? Many receptionists are rather brisk and business-like; this is acceptable. But a rude, obstructive receptionist who is unwilling to assist or explain may not bode well for a happy relationship.

You also ask whether the doctors do their own night calls or whether they use an agency. (If they do use agency doctors, you could find yourself being treated in an emergency by an unfamiliar doctor who does not have access to your medical records.) If you particularly want to be treated by a woman GP, find out if any of the doctors are women. Ask how long the average appointment is: good GPs allow ten minutes per patient. And ask whether you can be sure of getting an appointment within 24 hours if you want to see a doctor urgently.

CONTRACEPTION

If you want contraception on the NHS, you do not have to get it from your GP. For a variety of reasons, some people prefer to go direct to a family planning clinic. At such a clinic, you have a better chance of being seen by a woman doctor, and you can also get free condoms, which your GP may not be able to provide. (Some district health authorities now give GPs condoms for free distribution.) You do not have to be referred by your GP to a clinic, and the opening hours may be more flexible. However, most people do consult their GPs for contraception, and if health authorities continue to cut back on family planning clinic services, more will be obliged to.

To provide contraception on the NHS, a GP has to have taken a course in family planning and be on the FHSA's 'contraceptive service list'. If your GP is not on the list, you can make an appointment with one who is, even if you are not registered with that doctor.

FUNDHOLDING GPs

Since 1990, larger GP practices have been able to become 'fundholders'. This means that they are given a budget, or fund, by the regional health authority to buy many of the services – such as hospital treatments, outpatient services and diagnostic tests – which would usually be paid for by the district health authority. The fund is also supposed to cover most of the drugs GPs prescribe.

Fundholding was introduced by the government ostensibly as a way of increasing choice for doctors and patients, but it did so with a keen eye on controlling costs. The Department of Health has had little control over what GPs have spent on treatments and tests: making them stick to a budget might encourage them to watch the pennies.

It remains to be seen whether fundholding will generally work to the benefit or disadvantage of patients. Opponents of fundholding are concerned that doctors will be tempted to make decisions on the basis of what the budget can bear rather than on their patients' medical needs. Nevertheless the number of fundholders is increasing, and the Department of Health has encouraged this trend by making the option available to smaller practices – those with 7000 or more patients on their lists.

One of the clear advantages is that fundholding GPs have more choice in selecting hospital treatment for their patients. They make their own contracts with hospitals and do not have to go along with the deals which have been struck by their district health authority. This can mean less waiting time for operations. Fundholders can also pay for consultants to hold out-patient clinics at their health centres rather than in hospital. As well as providing quicker treatment, this can also be much more convenient for patients.

PRESCRIPTIONS

Even though medicines have taken up pretty much the same share of the total health services bill for many years, the government is very keen to stop the amount of the drugs bill from rising. GPs have fought very hard to prevent cash limits being imposed on their prescribing, but restrictions are likely to become increasingly tough.

There is already a 'restricted list' of medicines which GPs cannot prescribe on the NHS because the Department of Health regards them as too expensive and no more effective than less costly preparations. Although GPs have not yet been given a fixed cash limit on the medicines they prescribe, they are not supposed to exceed an 'indicative prescribing budget' – a figure which their FHSA sets every year. If they do exceed it, they get a visit from the FHSA's medical adviser who comes armed with a computer printout which analyses their prescribing habits. The medical adviser can insist that GPs go through this material to identify areas where they might reduce their costs.

One of the main reasons why health costs consistently rise more quickly than general inflation is that technology is continually coming up with better ways of diagnosing and treating disease. Doctors obviously want the best for their patients, but innovation comes at a price.

The most expensive drugs tend to be the newest ones. Manufacturers charge high prices for new medicines so that they can recoup their development costs and make a profit before their patent runs out. A recently launched migraine drug, for instance, costs about 20 times more than its nearest competitor, but despite its price, GPs have been keen to prescribe this drug because it has proved very effective for patients who have not responded well to the older migraine treatments. In theory, if every migraine patient were prescribed this medicine, the cost would absorb the whole current NHS drug budget! In practice, of course, not every patient will need the new drug, but its price is a major challenge to everyone involved in trying to control costs in the NHS.

On the other hand, new drugs are not always better than old ones, and their risks are less well known. There may sometimes be good medical reasons, as well as economic ones, for prescribing a tried and tested medicine. Also, when a medicine's patent has expired, any manufacturer can produce it. These 'generic' drugs usually cost much less than the same substance marketed under a brand name and doctors who are wise to this can make considerable savings by prescribing a generic version.

Until recently GPs have not had to worry about the cost of what they prescribe because the Department of Health always picked up the tab. Now that the DoH is handing more responsibility for watching costs to the doctors themselves, your GP may have to think twice before prescribing you an expensive medicine.

NEW CHARTER STANDARDS

The original *Patient's Charter* was extended at the end of 1992 to spell out the rights patients should expect from their GPs and FHSAs. The Department of Health also laid down new standards for FHSAs, especially in helping people who wanted to register with a doctor or change doctors. As of April 1993, the new Standards are:

- *Where a person is not registered with a GP, the FHSA must be able to find a GP for that person within two working days.*
- *To help people change doctors easily and quickly, the FHSA must despatch details of how to change and a list of doctors – to anyone who asks – within two working days.*
- *FHSAs must co-ordinate and publish information about local medical services, including the FHSA's own quality standards.*
- *FHSAs must transfer medical records quickly when a patient changes doctor.* (Records which are urgently required should be transferred within two working days, and routine transfers should be completed within six weeks.)
- *FHSAs must provide a full and open response to any comments, suggestions or complaints that people make about services.*

3

EMERGENCY MEDICAL CARE

The right to receive emergency medical care at any time, through your GP or the emergency ambulance service and hospital accident and emergency departments

A right to emergency treatment is all very fine, but when we are faced with an emergency, we need action. What do you do when your spouse has a heart attack, your toddler swallows bleach, your mother falls down the stairs, or your neighbour gets hit by a car? When speed is of the essence, what do you do? Call 999? Call your GP? Or take matters into your own hands?

It is often not an easy choice. Despite the new national Charter Standard that ambulances should arrive within 14 minutes of an emergency call (19 minutes in rural areas), it is no secret that in some parts, especially London, the service cannot deliver this promise. The time it takes for GPs to arrive will depend on their other calls – or the efficiency of a deputising service (i.e. agency doctors).

The problems of the emergency services are compounded by their misuse and abuse by the public. They are often asked to deal with people who do not need urgent treatment.

However, when you are faced with a real emergency which needs immediate attention, the ambulance service are the people to call. When you dial 999, tell the operator exactly where the patient is and what kind of problem you think he or she has.

DO-IT-YOURSELF RESUSCITATION

If someone's heart stops or if a child chokes on a peanut, you may not even have time to wait for the emergency services. But anyone over the age of ten can be trained in emergency resuscitation in a couple of hours. These courses tell you how to deal with choking and bleeding as well as heart attacks. In some American cities, notably Seattle, Washington, one in five of the population has been trained in resuscitation, and many heart attack patients have been saved by a family member or passer-by.

Training schemes here are run by branches of the British Red Cross and St John Ambulance Brigade; to find their number, look in your local telephone book. There is also the 'Bart's City Life Saver' project at St Bartholomew's Hospital in London (tel: 071-606 3669), and the 'Frenchay City Life Saver' project in Bristol (0272-753799);

in Brighton, there is 'Heartguard' at the Royal Sussex County Hospital (tel: 0273-676439). The British Heart Foundation's 'Heartstart' programme runs courses in many parts of the country and can advise people how to set up their own (tel: 071-935 0185).

WHEN TO CALL YOUR GP

If the emergency is not life threatening, call your general practitioner. GPs do not always have to visit patients at home, but their contracts oblige them to do so 'if the condition of the patient so requires'. In practice, what this means is that a GP will want to have a good idea of a patient's symptoms before turning out, even during normal working hours. They have to provide an out-of-hours service, too. As they obviously cannot work 24 hours of every day, this is usually arranged by a rota system, whereby doctors in a practice take it in turn to do late calls, or by using a deputising service. Some practices use both systems, using a rota system until, say, 2 am, then switching over to the deputising service. Deputising services can only employ fully qualified doctors, but these will not have access to your medical records, so you cannot expect the same degree of familiarity with your health problems which your GP may have.

ACCIDENT AND EMERGENCY DEPARTMENTS

The accident and emergency (A&E) departments in general hospitals provide a 24-hour service. Smaller hospitals may only have a casualty service, which is closed at night, while many specialist units have no facilities at all for emergencies coming 'off the street'. So if you are using your own transport to get to a hospital, find out first whether it takes accidents and emergencies.

As A&E departments have to deal with all sorts of patients

with all sorts of problems, most now use a system called 'triage' to sort out which cases need to be seen soonest. When you arrive, a nurse will assess the severity of your problem, decide whether you need immediate treatment, or give you an idea of how long you might have to wait. A&E departments do have the right to refuse treatment if your complaint does not need urgent medical attention and could just as easily be handled by your GP.

AMBULANCES

These are summoned by a 999 call. The demand for their services is considerable: more than two million patients use emergency ambulances in Britain every year. They should arrive within minutes, but the standard of service differs in different regions. Emergency ambulance crews are trained in emergency medical techniques. All ambulances should now carry defibrillators to stimulate the hearts of patients in cardiac arrest. Ambulance crews are also very skilled in handling accident victims. Should you ever be in doubt about moving someone who has been hurt – this applies particularly to people who may have damaged their neck or back – leave it to the ambulance crew.

If an ambulance is coming to your home, make the crew's task easier by giving accurate directions and by putting lights on in the front of your house. It is often impossible to read street numbers on front doors from a moving vehicle, especially at night.

Ambulance services, like hospitals, are now classified as service providers in the reformed NHS and have contracts with health authorities. Private ambulance services are springing up in many parts of the country, and some offer emergency services for a fee or annual subscription. However, they do not yet contribute to the 999 emergency service.

A final note: if you (as a driver or a passenger) have been in a road traffic accident, GPs and A&E departments are now entitled to ask you for a fee for treatment. This is a practice which has been agreed with motor insurance companies. If you are asked to pay, keep a receipt and claim the money back from your insurer.

CONSULTANTS

The right to be referred to a consultant, acceptable to you, when your GP thinks it necessary, and to be referred for a second opinion if you and your GP agree this is desirable

You do not have to study this 'right' very hard to realise that it does not promise a great deal. Your right to be seen by a consultant is not absolute: you cannot demand an appointment, even less a second opinion. Under the National Health Service, you only get access to a consultant via your GP. Indeed, even if you opt for private treatment, you will normally only get an appointment with a consultant if your GP refers you. The system works rather like the law, where you need a solicitor to approach a barrister on your behalf.

This is a peculiarly British system; in the United States or Germany, for instance, patients often go straight to a specialist without consulting their family doctor first. The advantages of the British system are that your GP knows your entire medical history, you may stand a better chance of seeing an appropriate specialist for your problem if your GP assesses it first, and he or she will be able to keep tabs on *all* your treatment. The disadvantage is that you may end up with less choice in the specialist care you receive.

Judging by a poll of patients conducted by the Consumers' Association (*Which? Way to Health*, April 1992), most patients have little say in the consultant they are referred to. More than 70 per cent said that their GP made the choice, and for most of them, that choice was made without any explanation or discussion. Only 12 per cent of patients said that their GP had discussed the choices available and allowed them to make the final decision.

So, as yet, choice is the exception rather than the rule. And that is unlikely to change unless patients actually demand more choice.

WHAT IS A CONSULTANT?

Consultants are specialists who have the expertise (and hopefully the facilities) to perform diagnosis and treatment which are beyond the scope of a general practitioner. While the GP has a basic grounding in most areas of medicine, consultants concentrate on particular diseases, age groups or areas of the body. The specialists to be found in a general hospital would include:

Cardiologist/cardiac surgeon: *diseases of the heart*
Dermatologist: *skin diseases*
Endocrinologist: *hormone problems*
ENT surgeon: *ear, nose and throat problems*
Geriatrician: *care of old people*
Gynaecologist: *women's reproductive problems*
Neurologist/neurosurgeon: *brain and nervous system problems*
Obstetrician: *pregnancy and childbirth*
Oncologist: *cancer care*
Ophthalmologist: *eye problems*
Orthopaedic surgeon: *bone and joint problems*
Paediatrician: *diseases of childhood*
Plastic surgeon: *reconstructive surgery*
Psychiatrist: *diseases of the mind and emotions*
Rheumatologist: *joint and muscle disorders*
Urologist: *bladder, prostate, and kidney surgery*

You will also find *general physicians*, who deal with a wide range of diseases including diabetes and allergy, and *general surgeons* who specialise in stomach and bowel surgery as well as carrying out simpler operations for hernias, haemorrhoids and varicose veins.

Among those you are less likely to consult directly as a patient are anaesthetists (though some anaesthetists do run pain clinics) and pathologists, who work behind the scenes helping with diagnosis by examining body tissues for signs of disease.

Traditionally, the consultant headed a small team, or 'firm', of doctors, which would include (in descending order of seniority) a senior registrar, registrar, senior house officer and house officer. That structure still exists in many places, though hospital doctors now tend to work in larger teams rather than small firms.

Hospital medicine is a pyramid-shaped structure, with the junior doctors at the base working long hours for relatively little pay while the consultants at the top generally enjoy more civilised hours and much higher earnings. Unlike GPs, consultants are salaried employees of the NHS, though they are allowed to take private patients. Many consultants work exclusively for the NHS, but those who do private work, especially if they are successful

surgeons, can easily double or treble their NHS earnings.
Consultants who are well thought of by their colleagues may also
get 'merit awards' – extra payments which can increase their NHS
earnings considerably.

GETTING TO SEE A SPECIALIST

So how does the referral system work? There are a number of steps
each patient must go through.

First, it is your general practitioner, not you, who decides
whether you need specialist attention. In the normal course of
events, this is not a problem: the GP will know whether your
condition is something he or she cannot deal with or has possible
complications which warrant specialist attention.

Some health authorities are trying to discourage GPs from
referring patients for expensive specialist treatment unnecessarily.
They have urged GPs to follow 'protocols', or guidelines on
diagnosis and treatment, which lay down what tests or therapies
should be offered to patients by GPs before referring them to
consultants. There has been some controversy about these
protocols: their critics have claimed that they are an attempt to cut
costs at patients' expense and could delay proper treatment. The
other side of the argument is that protocols are only a summary of
what is generally regarded as sensible, rational care.

The decision to refer rests on GPs' own professional
judgment. But what if your GP's judgment does not agree with
your own? Occasionally patients do disagree with their GPs about
the need for a consultant's opinion. The main reason why GPs
might refuse to refer a patient is that they believe they are the best
person to manage the illness. If you disagree, there is not a great
deal you can do except keep on asking. You could change your GP,
though that is best kept as a last resort.

Another approach might be to ask your GP if one of the
other doctors in the practice can be asked to give their opinion on
your problem. This is a reasonable request and, as long as you do

not make it sound as if you regard your doctor as a uncaring idiot whose opinions are worthless, it should not cause offence. Then again, if your condition persists, and your GP can do nothing further to relieve it, it would be hard to refuse your request for a specialist opinion.

Another area where trouble has arisen between GPs and patients is with complaints such as ME (myalgic encephalomyelitis). This is a condition characterised by aches and pains and lethargy, which has aroused much controversy. Some doctors regard ME as a psychosomatic complaint; such patients, on the other hand, do not care to be told that their complaint is 'all in their heads' and demand to be taken more seriously,

Before patients reject GPs' opinions outright, they should ask their doctors why they are sceptical. It may be that the GPs simply resent their patients coming and telling them, the doctors, what they are suffering from. Or patients might find that the GPs really do not know what treatment or advice to offer. If that is the case, a GP should always refer a patient: there are reputable specialists who deal with conditions such as ME. Sometimes doctors are right to be sceptical: many complaints have no physical origin but are caused by stress or anxiety and may respond better to counselling, which some GPs can provide. So before you decide to sack your doctor or rush off to a fringe practitioner – and there are plenty of those, only too happy to take your money for dubious therapies – do at least try to talk your problem through with your GP.

Irritable bowel syndrome is a condition which is often linked with stress. But its symptoms can be so upsetting that GPs will sometimes refer patients for a specialist opinion, if only to convince them that they do not have a more serious underlying disease.

That said, GPs do sometimes need to be chivvied into getting you an appointment with a consultant.

I went to my GP with a minor but embarrassing problem. She agreed that I needed an out-patient appointment with a consultant. Some three weeks later, I still had the problem, but I had heard nothing more about the appointment. When I went to see the GP about something else and shyly asked

about my other problem, she told me that she always waited till the patient came back to her a second time before she even bothered to write to a consultant. (London patient)

IS YOUR CONSULTANT 'ACCEPTABLE'?

According to the *Patient's Charter*, the consultant should be 'acceptable to you'. But how on earth do you know whether the consultant is going to be acceptable? Most people simply take their GPs' word for it. In fact, GPs who are not fundholders may not have a great deal of choice; unless they have very good reasons not to, they will have to stick with the consultants in the hospitals with which their district health authority has a contract. GPs who are fundholders will presumably have considered the quality of the consultants in the hospitals with which they have signed contracts, but even so, they are not usually going to want to send you somewhere else if it means more paperwork or cost. If you have any doubts, good questions to ask your GP might be:

- **Why have you chosen this consultant?**
- **Why is this consultant preferable to others?**
- **Would you refer me to this consultant if I had private health insurance and could chose the best available?**

Of course, if you have previously had treatment for a particular ailment, you are in a better position to know whether a consultant is acceptable or not. In the Consumers' Association poll cited earlier, nearly 90 per cent of patients were satisfied with their care from hospital doctors and nurses, but that still left 10 per cent who were not. If you do not like the service you receive, you should obviously make your feelings plain.

There are two main reasons why patients dislike consultants: (1) their manner; and (2) their clinical ability (or lack of it). Ideally doctors should be both well mannered and competent, but of the two qualities, competence is obviously the more important. Doctors with impeccable manners and great charm win their patients' hearts and are often very successful in private practice. This does not necessarily mean that they are very good at their job.

Assuming that you have no objection to the consultant, your GP writes to him (it probably will be a him: five out of six consultants are men) to request an out-patient appointment. If there is a chance that you have a serious condition requiring urgent attention, you will probably see the consultant very quickly. If not, you may have to wait: six weeks is the average waiting time for out-patient appointments. (This is far longer than you would have to wait in most European countries and is another reflection of the fact that we spend far less on our health service than other developed countries.)

The hospital will write to you, not your GP, telling you the time and place of your appointment. If travelling to the hospital is a problem because you have a disability, your GP should be able to arrange transport by ambulance or hospital car service. If you are hard up, you may be able to claim back the cost of your fares from Social Security (consult DSS leaflet H11: *Your hospital fares*).

The new national Charter Standards say that you should be seen by the doctor in out-patients within half an hour of your appointment time. Some district health authorities may set higher standards. However, in many busy clinics the sad truth is that patients often only get seen on time because others who have been given appointments have not turned up. If you cannot attend, try to tell the hospital as early as possible. If you do attend, it helps everyone if you arrive reasonably punctually.

In the out-patient clinic, it is quite possible that you will be seen by a registrar rather than the consultant. This is not necessarily a cause for concern or complaint. Registrars, especially senior registrars, are often as well qualified as their consultant boss, though probably less experienced. If you need an operation, it is also quite possible that it will not be performed by the consultant. Under NHS rules, you do not have the right to demand that the consultant, or indeed any individual doctor, performs your operation. In fact, you may not know who is going to operate on you until the day of the operation itself. The only way you can insist on being treated by the specialist of your choice is to opt for private treatment.

At the first out-patient appointment, the doctor will decide what treatment you need and whether you need to return for another appointment. If you need to be treated in hospital as an in-patient, you should be put on the consultant's in-patient waiting list. How long you will then have to wait depends on the urgency of your case and the number of other cases on the waiting list (*see* Chapter 9 on waiting lists).

The consultant then writes to your GP to explain what has been done and what may still need to be done. If your treatment is not something your GP is equipped to manage, you will remain under the consultant's care. Very occasionally the consultant may want to prescribe you a drug which can legally only be dispensed by the hospital. This will mean a trip to the hospital each time you need a new prescription. In most cases, however, your GP will take over responsibility for your care and for prescribing any medicines you may need.

There have been some instances where GPs have been unwilling to take over prescribing a particularly expensive drug recommended by a hospital consultant. The Department of Health guidelines say that the doctor 'who has clinical control' has the responsibility to prescribe.

SECOND OPINIONS

So far, so good. Or is it? Are you satisfied with what the consultant proposes to do for you? Do you understand exactly what it is? The next chapter of this guide will explain your right to have a clear explanation of any treatment proposed, but it is quite possible that, even if you think you have understood everything, you may have second thoughts. Even a confident, well-informed patient may find it hard to question or challenge a doctor in the unfamiliar surroundings of a hospital clinic. This could be the time you wonder whether you need a second opinion.

Most patients who ask for a second opinion are not

questioning the competence of the doctor. They just want to know whether they have been offered all the options. A typical example might arise when a consultant proposes doing an operation on a patient who would really prefer a less invasive treatment. If the consultant is a surgeon, he will tend to think in terms of surgical solutions and may be very persuasive as to their effectiveness. But the patient may wonder whether there is some other therapy, a drug perhaps, which might work just as well.

If you do not feel you have got a complete picture from the consultant, you should turn to your GP. A family doctor may not have the in-depth knowledge of a consultant, but should have some idea of the alternatives. The GP should also know which other specialists to ask for a second opinion. Before doing so, however, the GP will almost certainly want to discuss the options with the specialist you have already seen, if only for reasons of professional courtesy. After this, unless your GP thinks that what the consultant is suggesting is the only safe and effective option, it would not be unreasonable to expect him or her to arrange for a second opinion.

EXCEPTIONS TO THE RULE

Although your GP acts as a gatekeeper, deciding when and whether you need specialist treatment, there are important exceptions to this basic rule.

First, you do not need to be referred by your GP for treatment in any hospital accident and emergency department. If you have been involved in an accident, especially if you have lost blood or might have a broken bone, you may well need treatment or facilities, such as X-rays, which you GP may not be able provide.

Second, you do not need to be referred for treatment in a clinic for sexually transmitted diseases (STDs). Ever since these were set up to deal with the epidemics of syphilis and gonorrhoea which followed the First World War, they have operated a confidential, open–door policy which encourages people to seek treatment whenever they suspect they might have been infected, or even be running the risk of being infected. STD clinics, which are sometimes called departments of genito-urinary medicine or GUM clinics, can diagnose, treat and offer counselling to men and women on all sexually related diseases, including AIDS, and will generally be better equipped and more experienced than a GP at providing these services.

However, open access to A&E departments and STD clinics does not mean that you will necessarily be seen by a consultant. Most of the work is done by junior doctors with varying degrees of experience and specialist knowledge.

Finally, you do not have to be referred by your GP if you are seeking contraception or an abortion. Most GPs are qualified to provide contraception and are keen to do it as it earns them extra fees. However, you are still free to go to a local family planning clinic instead and do not need a letter from your GP to do so.

Abortion is available on the NHS, and your GP can help you get one if your case qualifies under the terms of the Abortion Act. However some GPs are unwilling for religious or moral reasons to refer women for abortions. If GPs do have such a conscientious objection, they are obliged to refer patients to a doctor who does not. But rather than broach the subject of abortion with an unsympathetic GP or face a delay waiting for NHS treatment, women may prefer to approach directly one of the charities which specialise in abortion counselling (*see* Reference section at the end of this book). About 50 per cent of abortions are carried out in the private sector.

CLEAR EXPLANATIONS

The right to be given a clear explanation of any treatment proposed, including any risks and any alternatives, before you decide whether you will agree to the treatment

A woman who had gone into hospital to have a minor gynaecological procedure awoke after the operation to be told that the surgeon had decided to remove her womb and ovaries instead. She had not given consent for this operation. She reported him to the police, and the case was referred to the Director of Public Prosecutions.

Once upon a time, patients may have been inclined to believe that 'doctor knows best' and accept their treatment without question or complaint. If it was ever so, it is not the case today. All medical treatment carries risks as well as benefits, and a good doctor will want you to know what you are letting yourself in for. This is not just a matter of politeness and consideration; there are good legal reasons for your doctor to make sure you understand and agree to the treatment you are given.

No one, in any sphere of life, is entitled to lay hands on you against your will without running the risk of criminal prosecution. If someone injures you, you also have grounds for suing them in the civil courts for assault, trespass or negligence. Medical examination and treatment come under the same law, and doctors and nurses do not have special privileges. Even if your life is in danger, you can refuse to accept treatment.

There are only two circumstances in which your legal rights in this area could be suspended: first, if you are mentally ill and have been detained under certain sections of the Mental Health Act; second, if you are suspected of having a dangerous 'notifiable' disease, such as tuberculosis or typhoid, you can be isolated from others who might be at risk. There are about 25 notifiable diseases, but only cases where the public is at risk of infection would call for the regulations to be enforced. Even so, although you may be forceably isolated, you still cannot be treated against your will.

This sounds simple enough, but in fact the law about consent to medical treatment is quite complicated. For patients who are mentally ill, consent is a difficult area. There are also enormous differences between doctors in the amount of information that they see fit to give their patients – and between patients in the amount of choice they demand.

HOW MUCH TO YOU WANT TO KNOW?

For instance, there cannot be many people who would be prepared to let their doctor decide what form of contraception they should use. Doctors may have a better idea of the benefits and drawbacks of each method, and they are expected to pass that information on in a clear, unbiased manner. But the choice should be up to the user.

On the other hand, when it comes to deciding which brand of antibiotic they should be prescribed, most patients would accept their doctor's decision without a second thought. This is not necessarily a good thing; it does doctors no harm to be asked why they are prescribing a particular drug – or indeed whether they should be prescribing a drug at all.

Almost all treatments carry a risk of some kind. A doctor should tell you about the side-effects a drug may have and should warn you of any risks you may run if, while taking the prescribed remedy, you take other drugs, eat certain foods, drink alcohol, drive a car or pursue any other normal daily activity. But the law does not oblige doctors to tell you every possible risk. Exactly how much information they give you is left to their own judgment.

Ten years ago, a survey of hospital patients found that 57 per cent were dissatisfied with the information they had been given about their treatment. Since then, a number of important legal cases have encouraged doctors to make more effort to ensure that patients are given the facts about their treatment. 'Even though a few patients don't want to be told,' says the British Medical Association's guide to medical ethics, 'there is now little justification for withholding information - unless to tell all would be clearly detrimental to the individual.'

However, ethics are not quite the same as legal obligations. The law says that doctors have a duty to disclose any *substantial* risk to a patient. But that does not mean that they have to disclose *every* risk.

If you were not told of the risks of a treatment and you suffer severe side-effects or complications, you could sue your doctor for negligence. If you did sue, you would have to convince the court that you had not been properly warned. You would also have to show that your doctor had not given you information that other doctors in a similar position would have given their patients.

In a celebrated case – Sidaway *v.* Bethlem Royal Hospital and others *– a woman sued the surgeon who had operated on her neck. She had been paralysed as a result of the operation. She claimed the surgeon had failed to tell her that the operation carried a one-in-100 risk of damaging her spinal cord. She said she would never have consented to it if she had known that such a risk existed. Before the case came to court, the doctor had died, and the patient, Mrs Sidaway, was unable to prove that she had not been told about the risk. Her case was dismissed. The Law Lords decided that a doctor could be judged negligent if he had failed to act in accordance with 'a responsible body of medical opinion'. But, unfortunately for Mrs Sidaway, there was no evidence that her doctor had failed to do so.*

The failure of Mrs Sidaway's case highlights the difficulty that any patient could have: proving they had not been told something they should have been told.

About 80 per cent of negligence actions brought against doctors fail in the courts. Nevertheless the subject of consent is a hot legal issue, and there is increasing pressure for doctors to reveal risks even when they are very small.

In Gold *v.* Haringey Health Authority*, a woman who had undergone a sterilisation operation sued for damages because* *she had become pregnant three years later. The surgeon had not told her that there was a risk that the operation might not work. The judge ruled that, in the circumstances, this was a risk which, however small, she should have been told about.*

In both the Gold and Sidaway cases, the actions were brought against the doctors for negligence and were heard in the civil courts. However, it could also be a criminal offence for a doctor to perform an operation without the patient's consent. This might arise if a surgeon performed a different operation from the one he had said he was going to perform, or if a patient had been browbeaten into undergoing an operation he or she did not really agree to. If a court decides that an assault has been committed, it can award damages to the victim.

CONSENT FORMS

Before patients undergo invasive procedures such as surgery or radiotherapy, they are usually asked to sign a consent form. The standard form used in the NHS gives the name of the proposed treatment or operation and states that its nature and purpose have been explained to the patient. It also has a second clause which gives consent for any other procedures which may prove necessary.

The second clause is not a 'catch-all'. It does not allow the doctor to change his or her mind and do something different. The clause is there simply in case the doctor has to deal urgently with some unexpected complication. So if you have given your consent for a D&C, you should not come round from the anaesthetic to find that you have received a hysterectomy. If you have been told that you are having a lump removed from your breast, the second clause does not grant the surgeon permission to perform a full mastectomy.

By signing a consent form, you are not signing away your legal rights. Obviously you should not sign before you think you really do understand the nature and purpose of your treatment.

However, if it does subsequently come to light that you were not told everything you should have been told, you still have grounds for complaint or legal action.

Patients are not usually given a copy of their consent form. Consumer groups say they should be. If for any reason you do need a copy, you should be able to get hold of the original by requesting access to your medical records (*see* Chapter 6).

Some hospitals now give patients written information about their treatment before they are asked to sign a consent form. This is a good practice because it can ensure that patients are reminded of any points which might have been forgotten or glossed over during a verbal explanation.

EMERGENCIES

Obviously, if you are unconscious, you cannot be expected to read a leaflet or sign a consent form. Doctors are entitled to treat unconscious patients whose lives would be in danger if treatment were delayed. However, they are only allowed to do what is strictly necessary to deal with the emergency, and whenever possible, permission is sought from the patient's next-of-kin.

CONSENT FROM CHILDREN

Doctors do not necessarily have to get a parent's permission to treat a child if, in the doctor's opinion, the child has a full understanding of the treatment in question. This could give a doctor the right, for instance, to prescribe the Pill to a 15-year-old girl. If the girl did not want the doctor to tell her parents, the doctor would be obliged to follow her wishes.

On the other hand, the law would not allow a doctor to vaccinate a toddler without its parent's consent. An infant would not be regarded as capable of making an informed choice.

If doctors believe that consent is being withheld unreasonably by a parent, they can apply for a court order. However, a court would be likely to grant permission for treatment of a child against its parents wishes *only* in life-and-death cases.

WHAT SHOULD YOU ASK?

It would be unfair to most doctors to suggest that information is something which has to be wheedled out of them and that patients should only give their consent with extreme caution. Generally speaking, doctors like to assume that their patients have confidence in what they, the doctors, are doing. However, they often have many demands on their time, and when time presses, corners may be cut. Some doctors are also not good communicators and find it hard to express themselves in simple, non-technical terms. So if you do have questions or worries, make sure they are heard.

● **Ask about side-effects and possible complications. How often do they occur? Could they do long-term harm?**

● **Ask how much experience the doctor has had with this treatment. Is it tried and tested? If it is new, do the benefits outweigh the risks?**

● **Ask what the alternatives might be. Are they less suitable for your condition? If so, why?**

● **Ask what would happen if you did not have this treatment. Would your condition get worse? Would it stay the same? Might it even clear up without any medical intervention?**

A competent, confident doctor should have no trouble with such questions.

IF YOU NEED PSYCHIATRIC CARE

According to MIND, the National Association for Mental Health, six million people in Britain seek treatment for their mental health every year. Those patients share the same basic rights as everyone else, and most of those admitted to hospital do so of their own free will.

However, some patients who have been 'sectioned' – committed for treatment under the Mental Health Act for their own safety or the protection of others – can be treated without their consent in certain circumstances. Sectioning requires the signature of two doctors (one of them a psychiatrist) as well as that of a psychiatric social worker or the patient's nearest relative. The special rules about treatment apply to people who have been sectioned for a period of 28 days or longer. They can be given nursing care (which might include restraint or seclusion) and drug treatment if a doctor thinks it necessary. After three months, medication can continue without the patient's consent only if a second doctor agrees that it is necessary. Electroconvulsive therapy (ECT) can also only be given with a second doctor's agreement. More invasive therapies, such as surgery or hormone implantation, can only be given with a second doctor's agreement *and* the patient's consent.

Patients who have been detained for assessment or treatment can apply to be discharged from hospital by approaching a mental health review tribunal. Tribunals consist of a lawyer, a lay person and a psychiatrist. Patients are entitled to have a solicitor present their case and may qualify for legal aid. The hospital administrator should be able to provide a list of solicitors. MIND can also offer practical advice and help in finding a solicitor.

WHAT IF YOU REFUSE TREATMENT?

Unless you are being treated under the Mental Health Act or – in very rare instances – by order of a court, you have an absolute right to refuse treatment. If you do refuse treatment, your doctor also has the right to discharge you from his or her care.

ACCESS TO RECORDS

The right to have access to your health records, and to know that those working for the NHS are under a legal duty to keep their contents confidential

It is really quite remarkable that there should ever have been any controversy about patients having access to their medical records. After all, there has never been much argument about people receiving bank statements or looking after the service histories of their motor cars. Are medical records so very different? And whose records are they anyway?

You may be surprised to learn that your NHS medical records do not belong to you or even to your doctor. Legally they belong to the health service. And although the recent Access to Health Records Act now allows you to inspect them, your rights are hedged around with a number of ifs and buts.

The main reason that many doctors were worried about the Act was that they had seldom written notes with the thought that patients might someday see them. Records were kept as an *aide-mémoire* for a patient's doctor and to provide background information for other doctors. The most serious worry expressed by the BMA was that patients could be distressed to discover facts about their health which their doctor had kept from them, possibly for the best of motives.

There were also less commendable reasons for keeping records secret. Some doctors had never felt any great need to be tactful or polite when writing about their patients. Notes might include all kinds of comments, some amusing, some defamatory, some inaccurate. Occasionally they would include disparaging codewords: the initials 'TATP', meaning 'thick as two planks', for example, or the mock Latin phrase *plumbum oscillans*, 'swinging the lead' (i.e. malingering). There was some concern that doctors might actually be sued for libel if such comments got into the wrong – i.e. the patient's – hands.

At the same time, research had shown that there were real advantages to be gained from letting patients see their notes. Doctors in Oxford and London who asked patients to check their own records found that as many as one in five contained errors. Many GPs had also encouraged mothers-to-be to keep their records if they were receiving antenatal care from them rather than at a hospital. As well as making the women feel more at the centre of things, this also allowed midwives and health visitors, who play as great a part in antenatal and postnatal care as the GP, to see the notes. It was generally agreed that this approach improved not only communication but also the quality of care as a whole.

The Data Protection Act 1984 allows people to see information about them which is stored on computer. Any organisation which keeps computer files on individual members of the public has to register this fact and allow people access, in person, to information which refers to them. Since 1987, patients have had the right to see any of their medical records which might be held on computer.

Although more and more medical records are being stored on computer, most NHS patients' records are still held in bulging little buff-coloured folders and are largely hand written. These records not only contain your GP's notes but also letters from specialists, laboratory test reports and so on. The Access to Health Records Act was intended to give you access to these records, too.

Due to lobbying by the BMA, the Act was a compromise. Patients are allowed access to their records but only to those written after the Act came into force in November 1991. The law applies to records held by GPs and hospitals, but it does allow a doctor or health authority to refuse access to any information which might – in the doctor's opinion – threaten the patient's mental or physical health if they were to see it.

HOW CAN YOU GET TO SEE YOUR RECORDS?

If you want to see your medical records, you have to make a written request to your GP (or health authority if you want to see hospital records). They have 21 days to respond. They are not allowed to charge you for the inspection, but you might be asked to pay for photocopying.

In practice, it might be hard to know whether some piece of information has been withheld. And if you want to check whether something written about you several years ago has been affecting your care ever since, you might not be able to find out if you are only allowed access to notes dating from November 1991.

On the other hand, some doctors are only too happy to let patients see their notes, however far they go back. They regard it as a valuable way of improving trust between them and their patients, eliminating errors and involving patients in their own care.

Another law – the Access to Medical Reports Act – allows you to see reports written about you by your doctor for insurance companies or employers. It is standard practice for insurance companies to ask clients to undergo a medical before taking out life assurance. Employers also want to know about the health of people they are taking on. This could be for a variety of reasons, from checking that prospective employees are up to the physical demands of the work to ensuring they do not have a drink or drug problem.

Before this Act came in, insurance companies expected normal rules of confidentiality to be stood on their head: the company got to see the report but the client was not allowed to. And employees obviously had reason to be concerned if reports contained information which could prejudice their job prospects.

Under this Act, you have the right to see a report before it is sent or up to six months later. If you tell your insurer or employer that you want to see the report *before* it is sent, the doctor has to allow you 21 days to see it. If you think it is factually wrong, the doctor is not compelled to change the report but does have to let you add your own written comments. You can still refuse to let the doctor send the report in; a doctor who passes on information without your written consent could be in breach of the rules of the General Medical Council (GMC), the body that regulates doctors. Of course, if you did prevent the doctor filing a report, your insurer or employer would probably draw the worst conclusions.

CONFIDENTIALITY

The wording of the *Patient's Charter* fudges an important distinction between the legal obligations and the professional ethics of people working for the NHS. In fact, there is no law which prevents doctors and nurses chatting about your medical problems to all and sundry. However, they do have strong codes of professional ethics enforced by disciplinary bodies which discourage behaviour of this kind (*see* Chapter 10 on complaints).

The General Medical Council states this basic rule in its 'blue book' on professional conduct for doctors:

Patients are entitled to expect that the information about themselves or others which a doctor learns during the course of a medical consultation, investigation or treatment, will remain confidential. Doctors therefore have a duty not to disclose to any third party information about an individual that they have learnt in their professional capacity, directly from a patient or indirectly.

As it stands, this rule would prevent a doctor passing on any information at all about a patient. But the GMC does allow a number of exceptions.

First, doctors are allowed to pass information on to other health professionals who are involved in treating a patient. They can also pass on information if they have the patient's consent, or even without their consent if the patient is too immature or incapacitated to be able to judge for themselves. If doctors suspect a child is being abused, for instance, they can inform the social services without the child's or its parents' consent. And the rules allow doctors to pass on information in cases of public interest, if failing to do so would expose the patient or anyone else to serious risk.

In some circumstances doctors may be legally obliged to pass on information: if they are ordered to do so by a court, or if their patient has a notifiable disease or is addicted to controlled drugs.

Obviously confidentiality is important, and medicine could hardly flourish without it. But all too often patients are the victims of confidentiality, because of doctors' refusal to give them information about their own conditions.

MEDICAL EXPERIMENTS AND TRAINING

The right to choose whether or not you wish to take part in medical research or medical student training

Ten years ago, women who had positive cervical smear tests were given an experimental radiation treatment at a leading cancer hospital. Months later, some of them began to experience a variety of unpleasant symptoms, and it was found that they had suffered severe internal damage caused by the radiation. The women say that they were not told that the treatment was experimental; the hospital says that they were. The woman have formed a support group and are seeking compensation.

Without medical research we would not have any of the benefits of modern medicine. While the greatest improvements in our health have come from better diets, clean drinking water and efficient sewers, the advances of scientific medicine follow close behind. Without them, life expectancy would be lower and the general level of suffering would be far higher. But medical research involves risks, and it is quite possible that you as a patient may be asked to share some of those risks.

At any time, tens of thousands of British patients will be taking part in medical research projects. Most will be involved in testing new medicines, but research in surgery, obstetrics and cancer therapy all need their guinea pigs, too. Some patients will not be trying anything new: one of the aims of research is to compare new therapies against tried and tested ones. Indeed some patients may not receive any active treatment at all: in many clinical trials, a new therapy is compared with a placebo, or dummy treatment. It is only by making such comparisons that the value – and the drawbacks – of a new treatment can be proven.

Patients in a research project who are given the placebo or the tried and tested therapy are referred to as 'controls' or the 'control group'. Patients may also be 'randomised', which means that they are allocated at random to the control or treatment group. In a 'blind' trial, patients do not know which group they are in; in a 'double blind' trial, the doctors do not know either. The point of all this rigmarole is to ensure that the trial is conducted as impartially and objectively as possible. The history of medicine is full of examples of therapies which were hailed as breakthroughs by doctors and patients alike, but subsequently turned out to be of transient or imaginary value.

While it is essential for new treatments to be tested this way, clinical trials pose a number of ethical problems. Apart from the potential hazards of giving patients experimental remedies, doctors have to consider the rights and wrongs of depriving patients of treatment by putting them into a placebo group. For this reason, doctors who want to set up clinical trials are supposed to have them cleared in advance by their hospital's ethics committee which decides whether the design of the trial is scientifically sound and whether its potential benefits justify the risks. There have been calls for ethical committees to include more lay members so that patients' interests can be better represented.

In short, your doctor's first duty is to you, the patient, not to medical research. Doctors should only ask patients to take part in trials if they genuinely do not know whether one treatment is better than another.

CONSENT

As a general rule, patients should be asked their permission before being involved in a clinical trial, and they have an absolute right to refuse. As with any other kind of treatment, there are legal safeguards which are supposed to ensure that patients know what they are letting themselves in for (*see* Chapter 5). However, clinical trials present more complicated legal and ethical problems than standard treatments, not least because there is a greater unknown element of risk.

The Department of Health's guidelines suggest that, if a patient is not expected to benefit from being involved in the trial, 'a full explanation of the proposed procedure should be given and the patient must feel free to withdraw at any stage'. If the patient is expected to benefit, 'consent should ordinarily be sought', but 'there are sometimes circumstances in which it is inappropriate or even inhumane to explain the details and seek consent'. This is a very grey

HOW DRUGS ARE TESTED

Potential new medicines go through exhaustive laboratory and animal testing, and many are rejected before they get to the stage of being tested on humans. Even then, the process of testing has barely begun. Tests on humans run through four main phases:

Phase One

Healthy volunteers are recruited to test the medicine. Its effect on a wide range of organs and physical and mental functions is tested.

Phase Two

A small number of patients – usually less than 100 – are tested with the medicine to find out what effect it has on their condition.

Phase Three

Clinical trials are conducted on large groups of patients comparing the medicine's effects against placebos and against other medicines used for treating similar conditions.

If the medicine is shown to be effective and acceptably safe, it will be granted a licence. Medicines intended for treating life-threatening illnesses for which there are few alternative treatments may get licences even if they produce quite severe side-effects.

Phase Four

Longer-term studies are carried out to monitor the medicine's safety and detect effects which may have escaped attention thus far (see section on post-marketing surveillance on pp. 59–60).

When a medicine has been available for some time, its manufacturers may come to believe that it has potential for treating another disease. Phases Two and Three would then have to be completed successfully before a licence could be issued for this new application.

area ethically, and doctors should not make decisions about such matters on their own. They should seek the judgment of an ethics committee first.

It is quite possible that doctors will want to play down the experimental aspects of a treatment, or indeed the fact that any kind of experiment is taking place. This might be the case, for instance, if a surgeon is trying a new technique. It may have proved successful in another surgeon's hands, but this might be the first time this particular surgeon has tried to do it. This is another ethical grey area. A competent surgeon will not shrink from revealing these facts. But with any procedure you might be asked to undergo, it does no harm to ask your doctors what first-hand experience they have had with it.

Drug companies have their own guidelines on how clinical trials of medicines should be conducted, and the European Community has chipped in with its own suggestions on how patients should be kept informed and how they should be compensated in the event of suffering adverse effects. But while they lay down the ground rules of good practice, these guidelines all lack legal bite and depend largely on the goodwill of those involved. If one patient, or especially if *many* patients were injured during a clinical trial and had possible grounds for claiming damages from a health authority or drug company, they would almost certainly have to pursue their claims through the courts. The sums involved could be large.

RESEARCH IN YOUR GP'S SURGERY

One of the most controversial areas of research is 'post-marketing surveillance'. It is also the type of research in which the average patient of the average GP is most likely to get involved.

Post-marketing surveillance is drug research which is under-taken when a medicine has already been through all the studies which were needed for it to be granted a licence by the Department of Health (*see box*). This process usually takes several years and will already have involved many hundreds, perhaps thousands of patients. So the medicine should be reasonably safe and effective.

However, experience with many drugs in recent years has shown that the full range of possible adverse effects only shows up when very large numbers of people have taken it for a considerable time. Opren, Eraldin and thalidomide are well-known examples of drugs which were heralded as great advances when they were released, but later turned out to have terrible effects on some patients.

Post-marketing surveillance was introduced – with the Department of Health's blessing – to cope with this problem. The idea was that doctors should closely monitor patients who have been prescribed a new drug and report back to the manufacturer on its efficacy and side-effects.

However, what seemed to be a good idea was turned by some drug companies into a way of boosting sales and stealing a march on their competitors. Doctors would be paid a fee for every patient on whom they filed a report. It might have been quite a modest fee, but they would mount up, and companies were able to offer doctors considerable inducements to switch their patients from a rival's product to their own. Independent drug experts noticed that some studies were not designed to elicit information of any great value, and suspicion grew that the system was being abused. Like some of the medicines themselves, the original good idea was found to have undesirable effects on some of its users.

Post-marketing surveillance continues, and in good hands, it may have good effects. However, in a recent review the Department of Health came to the conclusion that it had not contributed as much as had been hoped to drug safety. The General Medical Council has also warned doctors that they may be acting improperly if they accept payments for drug studies which have not been approved by the local ethical committee. Whether the GMC would actually strike a doctor off the register for this offence is another matter (*see* Chapter 10). However, the GMC has prosecuted a doctor who took fees for research work but deceived the drug company by returning bogus patient reports.

SHOULD YOU TAKE PART IN CLINICAL TRIALS?

Medicine will not progress if patients are unwilling to take part in research. Their willingness to take part will depend on their trust in their doctors. In October 1992, the Consumers' Association publication *Which? Way to Health* published a checklist of questions for would-be guinea pigs to ask their doctors:

- *What is the purpose of the study?*
- *What will happen to the results of the research?*
- *Can I have a copy of the results?*
- *What are the known risks and side-effects?*
- *Will I benefit from taking part in the trial?*
- *What can be done to make me better if I get a problem while taking part?*
- *What will I have to do if I take part? Will I need lots of blood tests? Will there be lots of hospital visits or forms to fill in?*
- *Will I be paid? Will the doctor be paid? By whom and how much?*
- *Has the trial been approved by a research ethics committee?*
- *Why is the new medicine thought to be an effective alternative to existing treatments?*
- *Can I have time to think about whether to take part?*
- *Can I have written details to take away with me?*
- *Would I get compensation if it all goes wrong for me?*
- *What will happen if I change my mind before the end of the trial? Are rebound effects likely when I stop?*
- *Would I be able to continue taking the medicine after the end of the trial if I found it useful?*
- *Will my health be monitored after the trial and, if so, for how long?*

Frankly, if your doctor is happy to answer all those questions to your satisfaction, he must really want you to take part! But there is nothing in that list which a prudent patient should not want to know.

MEDICAL STUDENTS

If you are being treated in a hospital attached to a medical school, you may be asked whether you mind having students observe your consultations or treatment. Most patients are prepared to agree to this, but you do have a right to say no. If you do not object, you may be asked to sign a consent form confirming your agreement.

If you think you might be embarrassed to discuss your intimate problems in front of students, bear in mind that a student might feel just as ill at ease as you do. It is by being exposed to real people with real problems that they learn how to do their job. However, if your doctor is likely to expose you to students, you should be asked your permission in advance.

Sometimes it is not the presence of one or two students which worries patients, but having to face a whole gaggle of them. You have reason to object if you are confronted by a large number of students without warning. Although you can refuse to have them observe, it is more difficult to do so if they are already there, waiting expectantly for the consultant to pronounce on your condition.

You should also be asked your permission if students are likely to be observing you when you are under anaesthesia. It was recently reported that students in some hospitals were getting their first experience in vaginal examination by carrying them out on anaesthetised women undergoing operations for completely unrelated conditions. If this sort of thing is done without your consent, it is an assault.

Patients are sometimes asked if they are prepared to attend student medical lectures to help the lecturer demonstrate the symptoms of a condition. This would probably only happen if the doctor were already familiar with your case; it is not likely to be sprung on you at a moment's notice.

Your legal rights do not extend to banning other qualified doctors and nurses from your consultations and treatment. Indeed, in certain circumstances, a doctor will insist on another doctor or nurse being present. If a male GP needs to do a gynaecological examination, for instance, he may ask for another person, almost always a woman, to attend as a chaperone. If your GP's practice includes a trainee, he or she will not be a student, but a qualified doctor who is learning the ropes of general practice before getting a second professional qualification. However, GPs do sometimes have students observing their practice, too, and you are as entitled to object to their presence during those consultations as you are in hospital.

INFORMATION ABOUT SERVICES

The right to be given detailed information on local health services, including quality standards and maximum waiting times

The government's avowed intention to bring the spirit of *glasnost* into the NHS is embodied in this clause of the *Patient's Charter*. Information is power, and in the past, patients have certainly been deprived of it.

The national health information line on Freephone (0800) 665544 is intended to offer patients facts and advice about many aspects of the NHS in their region. Though there is just one freephone number, callers are automatically connected to an information service run by their regional health authority or health board. Calls should be answered by a person, not a recorded message, and callers should be able to get information on:

● **NHS services: how to find a doctor, chiropodist, dentist, etc.**
● **Local Charter Standards**
● **Waiting times for operations**
● **How to complain about poor service**
● **Support and self-help groups**
● **General information on diseases and conditions**
● **How to look after your own health**

Some regions have been offering advice like this for some time. The Wessex Regional Health Authority, for instance, contracted the charity Help for Health to run a free advice service for patients, and the College of Health runs a similar service for the North East Thames Regional Health Authority (*see* Resources at the end of this book). These charities have a long history of campaigning for the consumer, and the quality of information they provide has been good. However, there will doubtless be differences between regions in the standard of service they offer.

The North East Thames Regional Health Authority is also providing (on the national health information line) a healthline service through the College of Health which gives recorded information on about 350 different conditions. This is also available to people outside the North East Thames Region, on (0345) 678444: unlike commercial medical advice services which charge premium rates (and often end up costing the caller as much as a paperback book), the College of Health lines are charged at local call rates. Whether other regions will make the free service available remains to be seen.

Since reorganisation, health authorities have had to collect information about the efficiency of their own services, and this information should be available to callers, too. The aspects of their service that health authorities now have to monitor include:

- **How long patients have to wait for outpatient appointments**
- **How long patients have to wait for treatment in accident and emergency departments**
- **How long patients have to stay in hospital for different operations**
- **How many operations are done as day-care cases**
- **How many operations are cancelled**

This information is being passed on to the Department of Health, which hopes to promote efficiency by highlighting authorities which appear to be doing well. Health authorities and fundholding GPs will have access to the information to help them decide which hospitals give best value. Like the school exam league tables published by the Department of Education, these comparisons may not always be entirely fair because they do not take into account many individual differences between districts. But they are a start.

What is needed next is more assessment of the quality of treatment itself. How many patients, for instance, have to go back into hospital due to complications or imperfectly performed operations? How many patients suffer from infections after surgery? How many need attention to scars caused by surgery? How well can patients walk after they have had hip replacements?

If you still want independent advice on health matters, the Patients Association and the College of Health can provide it, as can many of the hundreds of self-help groups (*see* Resources at the end of this book).

9

WAITING LISTS

The right to be guaranteed admission for treatment by a specific date no later than two years from the day when your consultant places you on a waiting list

If we were not so used to having to wait for treatment in this country, it would seem extraordinary that a government could reassure patients that it was their 'right' not to have to wait longer than two years. Why, you might ask, should there be any question of patients having to wait so long in the first place?

There are many reasons why waiting lists for hospital treatment differ in different parts of the United Kingdom, but there is one principal reason why we have them at all. That reason is not bad organisation, or a shortage of doctors or even some conspiracy by consultants to improve their chances of getting lucrative private work. Those reasons may play a greater or lesser part in determining how *long* waiting lists may be in the area where you live. But the principal reason why we have waiting lists is *lack of money*.

For many years, Britain has spent less on its health services than almost all comparable developed countries. This has not necessarily reduced the *quality* of medical care we receive (though some would question that), but it has reduced the *quantity* of care which can be provided at any time. So treatment is rationed, and when we need it, we often have to wait for it.

Waiting lists have been a hot political issue for more than 20 years, and their length has been used as a stick to beat successive governments for their lack of commitment to the health service. When extra money has been provided to reduce waiting lists – as in the years 1987 to 1991, when the government spent an extra £156 million to bring them down – they have fallen quite dramatically. Nevertheless short-term measures do not solve the underlying problem, and it is highly unlikely that waiting lists could disappear without a considerable long-term change in NHS funding. International comparisons show that we get relatively good service from the NHS, but we get it on the cheap. What we save in money, we spend in time on waiting lists.

HOW LONG DO YOU HAVE TO WAIT?

When the government published the *Patient's Charter* in 1991, the Department of Health claimed that 50 per cent of patients were admitted to hospital within five weeks and that 90 per cent were treated within a year. However, when these figures were published the money which had been spent on reducing waiting lists had been concentrated on the longest, most embarrassing lists, and almost all patients who had been waiting more than two years had been treated. There had also been considerable reductions in the numbers of patients waiting more than one year, but the numbers of those waiting less than a year had shot up.

The Department of Health has made a policy of targeting certain operations – e.g. coronary bypass, hip replacement, cataract removal – which can bring great benefits to patients and for which there is a great demand. But while these operations may be rather easier to obtain than before, other procedures still have extensive queues. How long patients have to wait differs enormously from speciality to speciality, and from district to district. Within hospitals, there can be vast differences between the waiting lists of different consultants. And even on an individual consultant's waiting list, some patients may have to wait longer than others.

There are all kinds of reasons why this should be. One of the most crucial criteria is how important and urgent the consultant considers the operation to be. The operations that patients have to wait for are largely those which doctors classify as 'elective' rather than urgent. A hernia, for example, may be distressing, but it does not usually become life-threatening. Varicose veins, which are even less of an urgent threat to well-being, might come that much further down a general surgeon's list of priorities. Whether or not surgeons actually encourage long waiting lists for these complaints in order to bump up demand for private treatment is a matter of some speculation. It would also be controversial to suggest that surgeons' decisions are prompted by whether they think a case is 'interesting' or 'boring'. However, it is true that operations for hernias and varicose veins are certainly less demanding for a surgeon to perform and may be less likely to command his professional attention than a procedure which he might find more technically satisfying.

Even more significant perhaps – and especially in the past – is the system under which each consultant is allocated a certain number of beds. Consultants would sometimes be reluctant to hand over one of 'their' beds to another doctor's patients and made efforts to ensure that 'their' beds were constantly occupied, even if this meant bringing in patients early or keeping them in hospital longer than might be strictly necessary. 'Bed-blocking', as this was called, restricted the flow of patients through the hospital system.

On the other hand, there can be very good reasons why a consultant has a long waiting list. If he is very good at his work, his services may be in great demand. A short waiting list is not necessarily proof that the doctor is particularly skilful and efficient.

HOW HAVE NHS REFORMS AFFECTED WAITING LISTS?

Since the NHS reforms were introduced in 1991, hospitals have been less inclined to put up with bed-blocking practices. Now that their income depends much more on the number of patients they treat, it is in their interest to move patients quickly through the system.

One way some hospitals are doing this is by encouraging day surgery. The Royal College of Surgeons has estimated that about 50 per cent of patients who undergo surgery do not really need to stay in hospital overnight before and after their operations. Currently only about 20 per cent of NHS operations are done as day surgery, but the proportion is increasing, and many hospitals have cut their waiting lists largely as a result of introducing more of it. The Audit Commission recently claimed that if all health authorities did as much day surgery as the dozen authorities which do it most, waiting lists in the UK as a whole could be reduced by a third.

Day care does not appear to be less safe than in-patient care, and as patients do not need food or a bed, it also cuts the 'hotel' costs of treatment and frees hospital beds for patients whose need is greater. All in all, this means that hospitals can treat more patients and offer treatment at lower cost to health authorities and fundholders.

Fundholding GPs are often in a better position to get quicker treatment for their patients. Some fundholders now pay for consultants to hold out-patient clinics at health centres, which is usually more convenient for patients than having to go to the hospital. Fundholders also have more freedom to arrange in-patient treatment as they are not bound by the contracts which their district health authority may have drawn up with local hospitals.

However, some of the changes brought about by NHS reforms may not be having the intended effect on waiting lists. Under the new system of 'purchasers' and 'providers', health authorities and fundholding GPs purchase treatments from hospitals. These purchasers estimate the number of treatments they will need and make a contract with the hospital to provide that number of operations at an agreed price. This system is supposed to encourage hospitals to get operations performed quickly and efficiently, and in many cases it has had this effect.

Problems can arise, however, when a hospital completes all the operations it has been contracted to perform well before its contract has expired. So if the health authority wants more patients to be treated, it has to find more money to pay the hospital. If it has already committed all its budget for that year, its only option is to make patients wait until the next financial year when it gets more money to pay for a new contract. In some instances, hospital departments have been stopped from taking on non–urgent cases because they have exceeded their contractual quota.

Here we have a good example of how waiting lists are caused, not by inefficiency, but by lack of money within the health service. Doctors find themselves doing less work than they could do, or would like to do, because money has run out.

Pressure from the Department to Health to reduce waiting lists has also led some hospitals to adopt rather dubious strategies to make it look as if their waiting lists are shorter than they really are. Hospitals and health authorities are given targets and incentives by the Department of Health to keep their waiting lists within limits.

If they fail to do so, they may be penalised. So hospitals which see their waiting lists rising may be tempted to fudge the statistics to make things look otherwise.

As far as official statistics are concerned, the time patients spend on a waiting list does not include the time they spend waiting for their first out-patient appointment. In fact, patients are only offically registered as being on a waiting list when their consultant has decided that they need to be admitted for treatment. So if the waiting list looks as though it may be exceeding the target set by the Department of Health, the consultant might be encouraged to put off the decision to admit the patient to hospital. The patient is 'reviewed in out-patients', which simply means they are kept waiting on an unofficial waiting list until the official waiting list is short enough for them to be put on it.

Waiting list figures may also look better if the district has a large number of fundholding GPs. As these have fixed budgets for purchasing hospital care for their patients, they may simply decide to wait until they have enough money in their budgets before referring some patients who could benefit from routine surgery. (This is more likely to happen towards the end of the financial year – between January and March – when funds are running low.) These patients would then not appear on hospital waiting lists and would therefore not appear in official figures either.

Strategies of this kind make official waiting list figures look better, but they conceal the truth.

EXTRA-CONTRACTUAL REFERRALS

Before 1991, GPs had the right to refer their patients to any NHS consultant who was prepared to treat them. They could take their pick of hospitals and consultants anywhere in the country and refer their patients to those they thought most suitable. GPs who are fundholders still have that right, but for the majority who are not, their ability to do this has been severely curtailed. GPs who are not fundholders must now refer their patients to hospitals with which their district health authority has a contract.

If waiting lists in those hospitals are unacceptably long, GPs can refer their patients to other hospitals, but only with the district health authority's agreement. They have to apply for an 'extra-contractual referral' (ECR). ECRs should not be difficult to obtain, but problems have arisen, especially when a district health authority has already spent the money set aside for ECRs in that financial year. According to the College of Health, some patients also find that their GPs have not heard of ECRs or are not prepared to fill in the necessary forms.

On the other hand, applying for an ECR can sometimes achieve unexpected improvements in the local service. In another case reported by the College of Health, a consultant who had been told that a patient was going to be referred elsewhere because of his long waiting list announced that he would treat the case as urgent and admit the patient within a few weeks.

HOW YOU CAN SHORTEN YOUR WAIT

You will only be put on a waiting list after you have had your first out-patient assessment with a consultant. This may be some weeks or even months after you have seen your GP about the problem. And even then it is possible that the consultant will keep your case 'under review'.

If you think that your consultant's waiting list is too long, your GP can find out whether you can be treated more quickly in another hospital. Sometimes a hospital not far from your home may be able to take you, but it is quite likely that you would have to travel to another part of the country. You may also be able to shorten your waiting time if you are prepared to go into hospital at short notice.

The College of Health operates a telephone helpline – (081) 983 1133 – which provides information on waiting lists all over the UK. Both GPs and patients can use the service. The College of Health can tell you where waiting lists are shortest, but your

GP will have to write to the consultant at that hospital to refer you. The helpline – a nationwide service – is partly funded by the Department of Health.

Regional health information services should be able to supply information on waiting lists in their own area on Freephone (0800) 665544.

GPs who are fundholders should have little difficulty arranging your treatment in a hospital outside your district. GPs who are not fundholders have to get permission for an extra-contractual referral from the district health authority.

Finally, do bear in mind that the length of a consultant's waiting list says nothing about his skill and expertise, nor his lack of them. A good doctor may be worth waiting for.

10

COMPLAINING

The right to have any complaint about NHS services – whoever provides them – investigated and to receive a full and prompt written reply from the chief executive or general manager

'Extremely complicated, slow, bureaucratic and weighted against patients' – these were the words chosen by the NHS's official consumer representatives to describe the health service's complaints procedure before the *Patient's Charter* was introduced.*

In its submission to the Department of Health, the Association of Community Health Councils pointed out that there were no fewer than seven different ways for patients to make complaints about health services. Far from making it easy to complain, this plethora of channels actually put people off. They did not know where to complain or how. If they did complain, it could take months before they heard whether anything had been done. And there were strong feelings that the system was not always independent or impartial.

One of the aims of the *Patient's Charter* was to make the NHS more 'responsive to patients' views and needs'. It is only likely to do so if patients can make their views known.

From April 1992, health authorities and hospitals have been required to publish regularly the number of complaints they receive and how long they have taken to deal with them. This kind of information will attract media attention, and this new obligation may help to ensure that complaints are dealt with more speedily.

WHY COMPLAIN?

The British have a reputation for being stoical, deferential people who don't like to make a fuss. These qualities do not serve us well when systems go wrong, when services are poor and when change is required. When complaints are justified, they should be made. If people do not make a fuss, things get worse.

As far as the health service is concerned, most patients are satisfied with the service they get most of the time. Most doctors are trusted, most nurses are held in high esteem. Most complaints

* From Citizen's Charter to Patient's Charter, *Association of Community Health Councils for England and Wales, August 1991.*

are about the failings of the system rather than the individuals who work within it. However, the old politicians' cliché that the NHS is 'the envy of the world' has now worn very thin.

Many of the NHS's problems can be put down to underfunding. As we have seen, we spend a great deal less on health services than other Western European and North American countries, and our expectations run ahead of what these limited funds can buy. We have had to get used to waiting lists; we may have to get used to some services, such as *in vitro* fertilisation and cosmetic surgery, being severely rationed. But we should expect that the quality of the care we do receive is not second rate. If it is not up to standard, we should complain, if only to prevent others suffering.

HOW TO COMPLAIN

If you do have a complaint, you are immediately faced with the problem of whom you should make it to. Hospital managers, family health services authorities, regional medical officers, the General Medical Council, the UK Central Council for Nursing and the Health Service Commissioner (ombudsman) all handle different sorts of complaints. If you believe you are a victim of medical negligence, you may want to talk to a solicitor.

If in doubt, the best place to start is your local *Community Health Council* (CHC). (Just to confuse us, they are called Local Health Councils in Scotland and District Committees in Northern Ireland.) Their number will be in the telephone directory. CHCs were set up to represent patients' interests. They are made up of members of the public, who are unpaid, and have a small – usually very small – full-time staff. They do have not much money or resources, but they can tell you how and where to complain. They may be able to help you draft a letter; they may provide an 'advocate' to act on your behalf. Advocates in this context are not lawyers; they are volunteers who help people with disabilities, language problems or other difficulties which might make it hard for them to present their own case.

You can also make a complaint on behalf of someone else, if they are too young, ill or infirm to act for themselves, or if you think someone who has died did not receive the treatment they deserved.

The national health information line on Freephone (0800) 665544 should also be able to give basic advice about how to make a complaint.

COMPLAINTS ABOUT GPs DENTISTS, OPTICIANS, PHARMACISTS

If you have a complaint about any of these practitioners, you should turn to your local *Family Health Services Authority* (FHSA), or Health Board if you live in Scotland or Northern Ireland. The address should be on the front of your medical card or in the telephone book. If you write, address your letter to the General Manager. You can ask for a complaint to be treated formally or informally. Either way, you should make your complaint within 13 weeks of the event you are complaining about. (Whether 13 weeks is long enough is open to debate. Until recently it was only 8 weeks.)

Informal complaints can be made about any aspect of the service you received, while formal complaints can only be made when you are claiming that the practitioner failed to act according to the terms of his or her health service contract. What this means in practice is that you can make a formal complaint about a GP who failed to provide treatment when you needed it, but not about rudeness or other bad behaviour. (If a doctor's behaviour is particularly obnoxious, you might consider a report to the General Medical Council, whose activities are described later.)

If you ask for your complaint to be treated informally, the FHSA may try to iron things out by talking to you and the practitioner. You should then receive an explanation or apology.

If you make a formal complaint, and if the FHSA thinks the practitioner may have been in breach of contract, there will be an official investigation. Your complaint will be heard by a panel of lay FHSA members, doctors and other practitioners. You can attend the hearing to present your case, with your advocate if necessary. If the panel decides that the practitioner has broken his or her contract, it can give a warning or deduct money from their pay. Afterwards you will be given a copy of the decision the panel has reached. If you do not agree with the decision (three out of four complaints against GPs are not upheld by FHSAs), you can appeal to the Secretary of State for Health, if you live in England, or the Secretary of State for Scotland, Wales or Northern Ireland, if you live there.

The Department of Health has laid down new Charter Standards for complaints. As of April 1993, FHSAs should acknowledge all complaints, comments and suggestions within two working days. Informal complaints should normally be cleared up within a month, and formal complaints within six months. Until the matter is cleared up, the complainant and the practitioner should both be given regular monthly progress reports on what is being done.

COMPLAINTS ABOUT HOSPITAL TREATMENT

If something niggles you on the ward or in out-patients, tell your doctor, the sister or charge nurse and see if the matter can be sorted out on the spot. If that fails to give satisfaction, ask for the name of the *designated officer* who deals with complaints – every hospital is supposed to have one. If you cannot find out who this is, address your complaint to the *hospital manager* (or the *chief executive*, if the hospital is an NHS trust) or the *general manager* of the health authority. As with family health services authority complaints, you should write within 13 weeks; you should get a 'full and prompt' written response.

If you do not get a satisfactory response, take your complaint to the *chair of the health authority* and/or to the *chief executive of the NHS* at the Department of Health, Quarry House, Quarry Hill, Leeds LS2 7UE.

Prolonged bungling or a persistent refusal to deal properly with the facts of your case may warrant a report to the *Health Service Commissioner*, better known as the 'Health Ombudsman'. The Ombudsman's job is to investigate administrative failures, and if he thinks the case warrants it, he can call for records to be produced and for NHS staff to appear before him.
The Ombudsman cannot deal with allegations of medical negligence against doctors. (Addresses for the Health Service Commissioners for England, Scotland and Wales are on p.104.)

A woman suffering from acute arthritis was angry when her GP refused to refer her to a specialist and told her that an ointment was all she needed to relieve her pain. She made a complaint to the FHSA, which took two years to hold a hearing before dismissing her complaint. She reported this to the Health Ombudsman, who decided that the FHSA had acted wrongly and was guilty of maladministration. The patient received no recompense for her trouble, but was pleased that someone had finally taken her complaint seriously.

GENERAL MEDICAL COUNCIL (GMC)

This deals with complaints about doctors who have acted 'improperly'. The GMC has the power to suspend doctors or strike them off the medical register, and the thought of being reported to this fearsome body would make most doctors anxious.

However, in practice the GMC only takes action against doctors who may have been guilty of 'serious professional misconduct'. Those who persistently neglect their duties, make sexual advances to patients, commit fraud or consume so much alcohol or drugs that they are no longer competent to practise may well find themselves up before the GMC's Professional Conduct Committee. However, the GMC very seldom investigates complaints about medical treatment unless the doctor has also acted improperly in some other way. This may change: moves are now afoot to extend the GMC's powers to discipline incompetent doctors.

If you do make a complaint to the GMC, it goes through a screening system which ensures that only the very worst cases of bad behaviour get as far as a formal hearing before the Professional Conduct Committee. Most complaints get no further than the 'preliminary screener', either because the screener thinks they are not serious enough or because there does not appear to be enough evidence to make the charge stick. If you make a complaint about diagnosis or treatment, you will almost invariably be told to take it up with the health authority first.

If the screener does think the case is serious, the person making the complaint will be asked to make a sworn statement, and the case will then be considered by the GMC's Preliminary Proceedings Committee. This decides whether to drop the case, send the doctor a warning letter, pass it to the Health Committee, which deals with doctors who are too sick to practise safely, or pass it to the Professional Conduct Committee.

Most complaints which come up before the Professional Conduct Committee have already been through the courts or have been referred by an FHSA after the doctor has been found guilty of an offence. Few complaints from individual members of the public ever reach this stage. The committee's hearings are held in public and are covered by the press – in great detail if they involve allegations of salacious or bizarre behaviour.

Critics of the GMC have long complained that the Council should be more prepared to consider complaints about poor medical care. A new procedure for handling such complaints has been proposed, but is unlikely to be introduced for some time. And although the GMC does now have lay members on its committees, it has been accused of being too dominated by doctors who are unwilling to act against their professional colleagues. (An eye-opening account of the way the GMC works has been written by Jean Robinson, who has been a lay member of the GMC for 20 years. See 'Further reading' at the end of this book.)

Incidentally, the GMC is often confused with the British Medical Association (BMA). The BMA has many functions, the main one being to negotiate with the government on doctors' pay and contracts, but it does not discipline doctors. While all doctors must be registered with the GMC, they do not have to be members of the BMA, and many are not. So, in short, there is nothing to be gained from complaining to the BMA.

Complaints about the professional conduct or competence of nurses, midwives and health visitors should be made to the *United Kingdom Central Council for Nursing, Midwifery and Health Visiting*. Complaints about dentists should be referred to the *General Dental Council*, which operates in most respects like the GMC. (For addresses, see pp. 104–5.)

COMPLAINTS ABOUT MEDICAL NEGLIGENCE

If you think that you have been a victim of negligent or incompetent treatment – or someone you care for has – you should first take it up with the doctor in question or their superior. If you were being treated in hospital, your GP may be able to lend valuable support. If you do not get a satisfactory explanation, take the matter up with the health authority, or the FHSA if it is a complaint about a GP.

When things do go wrong, doctors are sometimes unwilling to admit they could be responsible. Worried about possible legal action, they clam up, and are sometimes encouraged to say nothing by their health authority or the defence society which insures them against claims for negligence. This often has the effect of making the patient even more upset and angry.

If you are not satisfied with the response you get from your doctor or the authority, you can take your case to the *regional medical officer* at the regional health authority. The RMO, if he or she sees fit, can arrange for two consultants from another region to meet you and consider the case. There will be no lay people at this hearing, and you are not entitled to get a copy of the report the consultants make. Not surprisingly, this procedure also has its critics, both from consumer organisations and the medical profession itself.

If all else has failed, or if you think you should be awarded damages for what has happened to you, you may have to consider taking legal action. Your CHC or local Citizens Advice Bureau should be able to put you in touch with a solicitor who is prepared to offer initial advice for a small fee and can advise you whether you qualify for legal aid. Alternatively *Action for Victims of Medical Accidents*, who have considerable experience in this field, can also provide advice (*see* Resources for their address).

It can be a harrowing business taking your complaint to law. First, you will have to prove that you have been harmed as a result of the doctor's action; then, if you have been a victim of a mistake or an unforeseen consequence of treatment, you may not be awarded damages unless the doctor can be proved to have been negligent. If your case is strong, you may be offered an out-of-court settlement. Cases which do go to court generally go against the patient, which can leave you with a ruinous bill to pay. Doctors, on the other hand, have their costs covered by their medical defence society.

However much *glasnost* the *Patient's Charter* may have introduced, the sad fact remains that, throughout the whole complaints systems, the dice are still loaded against the person who complains. Don't let this put you off: by keeping silent, you only encourage further abuse and incompetence.

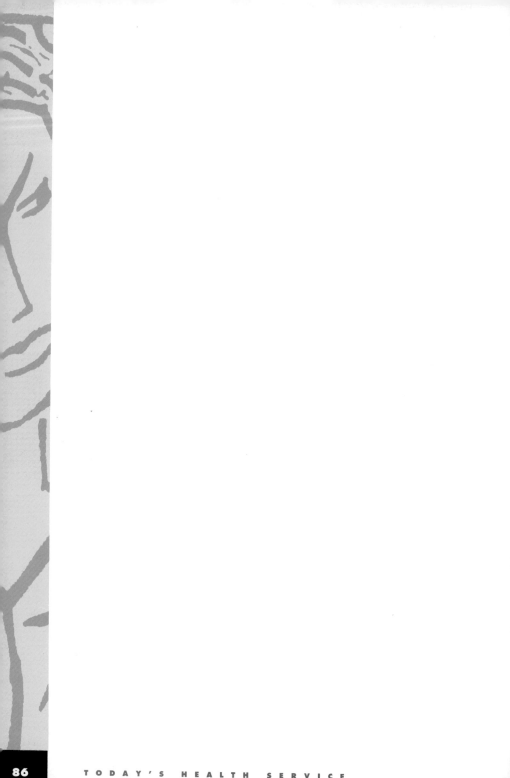

11

TREATMENT OUTSIDE THE NHS

Outside the NHS, private and complementary medicine flourish, largely unrestricted by the problems and regulations which constrain the state service.

As a rule, patients go for private medicine because it can often provide specialist treatment more quickly than the NHS, and patients can be sure that they will be treated by the consultant of their choice. People seek complementary, or alternative, medicine for a variety of reasons. The main ones are a dislike of drugs and medical technology, but they may simple believe that orthodox medicine does not have a cure for their problem.

Nevertheless both private and complementary medicine offer patients fewer rights than the NHS, and you will have little recourse if the service is not to your satisfaction.

PRIVATE MEDICINE

Although private medicine is far less developed in the UK than in most other Western European countries, there are now about 200 private hospitals with surgical facilities as well as several thousand nursing and residential homes and a number of private psychiatric clinics.

About 15 per cent of non–urgent (i.e. 'elective') surgical operations are performed in the private sector, but not all of them are done in private hospitals. Most large NHS still have 'pay beds', most of them in single rooms. For your money, you should get privacy and perhaps rather more palatable food than the standard NHS fare. NHS hospitals do not have separate operating theatres and clinics for private patients: apart from your accommodation and food, your treatment will be the same as an NHS patient's. Most doctors who do private practice are also NHS consultants.

The great majority of patients who opt for private treatment already have health insurance cover with BUPA, Private Patients Plan, Western Provident or some other insurer. If you are contemplating private treatment and do not have insurance, be sure to get – *in advance* – an estimate of what it is going to cost.

If privacy is more important to you than luxury, you might save yourself a lot of money by asking for an NHS 'amenity bed'. These are beds in single rooms, often a side room close to the main ward, and generally without the TV, telephone and minor luxuries you might expect in a private room. They are not private beds and you cannot usually book them, but they are sometimes available free or for just a small charge. Many NHS hospitals have them, but they are usually allocated on a 'first come, first served' discretionary basis, with priority being given to patients whose condition warrants privacy.

The charges can run to many hundreds, sometimes thousands of pounds: you pay not only for the consultant, the anaesthetist, medicines and dressings, but also substantial charges for your accommodation. Even if you do have insurance cover, check how much it actually does cover. Lower-cost schemes may not pay for the 'hotel' charges of the more luxurious hospitals. Nor do most schemes cover obstetric care, prolonged psychiatric treatment or cosmetic surgery. Most doctors work for standard fees which are agreed between the BMA and the major insurers, but fashionable doctors may charge very fashionable fees.

You will be faced with the same problem selecting a consultant as any NHS patient. Unless you happen to know of a suitable specialist, you will need to turn to your GP for advice. And in any case, a specialist will only accept you if you are referred by your GP. The General Medical Council does keep a list of approved specialists, but for its own reasons, it does not make this list available to the general public.

Information about private hospitals and the facilities they provide is available from the Independent Health Care Association, 22 Little Russell Street, London WC1A 2HT, tel: (071) 430 0537. But they cannot advise you about individual doctors.

COMPLEMENTARY MEDICINE

Complementary medicine used to be called 'alternative medicine', but most of its practitioners now prefer to put themselves forward as an addition to orthodox medicine rather than as rivals.

Complementary medicine has grown enormously in popularity over the past decade, despite considerable controversy about its effectiveness. Some complementary specialities, notably osteopathy and chiropractic, are practised by well-trained professionals who have carved themselves a generally deserved reputation in areas – such as the treatment of back pain – where orthodox medicine has often been weak. At the other end of the spectrum, there are many complementary therapists offering treatments which have more in common with magic than science.

For some patients, this may not matter. What they are seeking is a therapist who can offer them more time, attention or even magical mystique than a conventional doctor. For instance, aromatherapy, spiritual healing and reflexology may all help to ease an aching body and stressed psyche in ways an orthodox doctor would not dream of.

However, the skills and qualifications of therapists vary enormously. Although the law forbids unqualified people from practising as doctors, there is no such control over complementary therapists. Proposals are afoot to control the use of the titles 'osteopath' and 'chiropractor', but there are still many poorly qualified therapists who call themselves such, and the law as it stands now can do little about it. In some cases, qualifications may not matter much: healing by the laying on of hands, for example, is not something that people necessarily do better with years of academic study behind them.

However, there are organisations which offer information about complementary therapies and can give some guidance towards finding a therapist who has been through some recognised form of training. The Institute for Complementary Medicine (PO Box 194, London SE16 1QZ, tel: 071-237 5165, send self-addressed envelope plus stamps) and the Council for Complementary and Alternative Medicine (179 Gloucester Place, London NW1 6DX, tel: 071-724 9103) can advise on the more reputable bodies and their membership.

Although complementary medicine as such is not generally available on the NHS, an increasing number of doctors, mostly GPs, practice alternative therapies, with acupuncture and homoeopathy being particular favourites. In addition, a few GP practices and hospital rheumatology and orthopaedic departments employ the part-time services of osteopaths.

Homoeopathy is the only alternative therapy which is established in the NHS – and this is one therapy that insists it is an *alternative* to orthodox medicine. Although it stands the principles of orthodox medicine on their head (patients are given sub-molecular doses of remedies which, in larger amounts, might provoke the very symptoms the patients are suffering from), it is supported by a dogged minority of doctors. There are homoeopathic hospital facilities in London and Glasgow. The Homoeopathic Trust (2 Powis Place, London WC1N 3HT, tel: 071-837 9469) can provide a list of medically qualified practitioners.

●

There may be many exciting choices to make in complementary medicine, but there is even less protection against ignorance and incompetence. Choose wisely, choose well. And whether you go private or complementary, always bear in mind that old legal watchword: *Caveat emptor* – let the buyer beware.

REFERENCE

THE PATIENT'S CHARTER

The *Charter* lays down patients' rights and a number of standards which are expected of the health services. What these rights mean is covered in the main part of this book, but here is a summary.

The *Charter* spells out seven rights that already existed for patients:

1 To receive health care on the basis of clinical need, regardless of ability to pay.

2 To be registered with a GP.

3 To receive emergency medical care at any time, through your GP or the emergency ambulance service and hospital accident and emergency departments.

4 To be referred to a consultant acceptable to you, when your GP thinks it necessary, and to be referred for a second opinion if you and your GP agree this is desirable.

5 To be given a clear explanation of any treatment proposed, including any risks and any alternatives, before you decide whether you will agree to the treatment.

6 To have access to your health records, and to know that those working for the NHS are under a legal duty to keep their contents confidential.

7 To choose whether or not you wish to take part in medical research or medical student training.

The *Charter* then introduces three new rights, which reflect new government policy:

1 **To be given detailed information on local health services, including quality standards and maximum waiting times.**

2 **To be guaranteed admission for treatment by a specific date no later than two years from the day when your consultant places you on a waiting list.**

3 **To have any complaint about NHS services – whoever provides them – investigated and to receive a full and prompt written reply from the chief executive or general manager.**

An extension to the *Patient's Charter*, introduced in late 1992, lays down a further six rights which apply to GP services. You now have the right:

1 **To change doctors easily and quickly.**

2 **To have appropriate drugs and medicines prescribed.**

3 **To be offered a health check on joining a doctor's list for the first time.**

4 **If between 16 and 74 and have not seen your doctor in the previous three years: to have the health check to which you are entitled under the existing health promotion arrangements; and to be offered a yearly home visit and health check if 75 years old or over.**

5 **To be given detailed information about local family doctor services through your family health services authority's local directory.**

6 **To receive a copy of your doctor's practice leaflet, setting out the services he or she provides.**

CHARTER STANDARDS

The *Charter* set a number of national Charter Standards and suggested that health authorities, FHSAs and GPs should also publicise their own local standards. Some of the standards concern themselves with the way people should be treated and the standards of behaviour they should expect from NHS staff, while others are more quantitive measures.

The national Charter Standards are:

1 *Respect for privacy, dignity and religious and cultural beliefs.* Patients' dietary requirements should be met, and private rooms should be available for confidential discussions with relatives.

2 *Arrangements to ensure that everyone, including people with special needs, can use services.* This includes ensuring that buildings are accessible to people in wheelchairs.

3 *Information to relatives and friends.* Health authorities should ensure that, if you wish it, friends and relatives are informed about the progress of your treatment.

4 *Waiting times for the ambulance service:* 14 minutes if you live in an urban area, 19 minutes in a rural area.

5 *Waiting time for initial assessment in accident and emergency departments:* you should be seen immediately and your need for treatment assessed.

6 *Waiting time in out-patient clinics:* you should be given a specific appointment time and be seen within 30 minutes of that time.

7 *Cancellation of operations:* Your operation should not be cancelled on the day you are due to arrive in hospital, though this

could happen due to emergencies or staff sickness. If your operation has to be postponed twice, you will be admitted to hospital within one month of the date of the second cancelled operation.

8 A named qualified nurse, midwife or health visitor to be responsible for each patient.

9 Discharge of patients from hospital. Before you are discharged, a decision should be made about any continuing health or social care you may need, and if necessary, any arrangements for this should be made.

CHILDREN IN HOSPITAL

Action for Sick Children (formerly the National Association for the Welfare of Children in Hospital) has drawn up its own charter for children in hospital. Although it does not have any formal backing in law, the Department of Health has suggested that 'purchasers' should pay heed to it when drawing up their local Charter Standards. If your hospital does not meet the ASC standards, you may have good reason to ask why not.

1 All children should have equal access to the best clinical care.

2 Parents have responsibility for their children, and shall receive positive and appropriate support to care for their sick children both at home and in hospital.

3 Children and their parents shall be given full information about treatment and participate in all decisions.

4 Whenever possible, sick children shall be cared for at home, unless the care they require can only be provided in hospital.

5 **Staff caring for children, whether in hospital or in the community, shall be specifically trained and fully aware of children's emotional and development needs.**

6 **Children shall be cared for in an environment furnished and equipped to meet their requirements, whether in hospital or in the community.**

7 **No child shall be cared for in an adult ward.**

8 **Every hospital admitting children shall provide overnight accommodation for parents free of charge.**

9 **Parents shall be positively encouraged to be with their child in hospital at all times and to participate in their care.**

10 **Every child in hospital shall have full opportunity for play, recreation and education.**

The most common failing is for hospitals to put children in adult wards. A survey by Action for Sick Children (then NAWCH) in 1987 found that a quarter of all children in hospital, and over 60 per cent of those over 12, were treated in adult wards.

DISABLED PEOPLE IN HOSPITAL

The Royal College of Physicians and the Prince of Wales' Advisory Group on Disability have published a quite comprehensive *Charter for disabled people using hospitals.* This does not have formal government backing, though it, too, could be a useful yardstick for future national and local Charter Standards. It also contains a great deal of practical guidance on the needs of disabled people. The *Charter* is too long to include here in full, but these are its key principles:

- **Disabled people who use hospitals must receive appropriate understanding of their individual needs.**

- **Disabilities must not be aggravated by any procedures, treatment or unnecessary regulations.**

- **Hospital staff need to distinguish between managing an illness and working with a disabled person.**

- **A person who has learned to live with a disability is usually much better informed about it and the way to live with it than anyone else.**

The text of *A Charter for disabled people using hospitals* (ISBN 1-873240-37-6) is available from the Royal College of Physicians, 11 St Andrews Place, London NW1 4LE.

ORGANISATION OF THE NHS

The *Secretary of State for Health* heads a department of more than 5000 civil servants. The Department of Health's *Policy Board*, which is chaired by the Secretary of State, is made up of senior officials and people from industry and from the health service. The board decides the strategy of the health service. That strategy is put into effect by the *NHS Management Executive*. This is chaired by the Chief Executive and includes civil servants and people from within and outside the health service.

   Regional health authorities (RHAs) distribute funds to district health authorities, family health services authorities and fundholding general practitioners. There are 14 RHAs in England. Their main functions are to decide how resources should be allocated, to keep an eye on how efficiently services are being run and to mediate in any disputes between 'purchasers' and 'providers'.

   District health authorities purchase services for their local population and manage hospitals, apart from those which have become NHS trusts.

NHS trusts report directly to the Department of Health; they earn their income principally from contracts with district health authorities and fundholding GPs.

Family health services authorities (FHSAs) – of which there are 90 in England – usually serve the same community as the local district health authority. Their main function is to ensure that GPs, dentists, pharmacists and opticians do their work and are paid for it. They also handle complaints about family practitioners and provide information on local services.

Special health authorities, which include the Health Education Authority and the authorities which run London's postgraduate teaching hospitals, are not part of the main NHS structure. They report directly to the Secretary of State.

ORGANISATION OF THE NHS IN ENGLAND

Community health councils (CHCs) are statutory bodies which represent consumer interests and provide advice and information to the public. Their members are appointed by local authorities, voluntary organisations and RHAs. They have tiny budgets and the influence they exert relies more on persuasion than any statutory power.

In Wales, Scotland and Northern Ireland, the structure of the health service is rather different. The Welsh Office, Scottish Office and Northern Ireland Office, each of which is headed by its own Secretary of State, are responsible for health services. There are no regional health authorities. Wales has nine district authorities and eight FHSAs. Scotland has 15 Health Boards which combine the role of district health authorities and FHSAs. In Northern Ireland, the four Health and Social Services Boards also look after personal social services.

RESOURCES

FURTHER READING

The Health Care Consumer Guide by Robert Gann, Faber. Wide-ranging, readable handbook.

The New National Health Service by Chris Ham, Radcliff Medical Press. A factual guide to the NHS reforms, organisation and management.

The NHS A–Z, compiled and published by the Help for Health Trust. Very comprehensive looseleaf guide, intended for hospitals, general practices, CHCs, libraries.

A Patient Voice at the GMC by Jean Robinson, Health Rights.

The Patient's Charter, HMSO.

Safe and Sound by Linda Wolfe, Hodder & Stoughton. A reference book for parents on first aid and family emergencies.

Which? Way to Health, published by the Consumers' Association, is a monthly magazine on consumer health matters.

USEFUL ORGANISATIONS

This list is by no means complete; there are numerous other self-help groups and voluntary organisations that might be useful to you. Use this resource section as a starting point. Even if you think one organisation might not be right, ring them just in case – if they can't help you, they will often be able to recommend someone who can. Your local Citizens Advice Bureau may also be able to help.

Comprehensive directories of groups and organisations are included in the following publications, available at your local reference library.

The Voluntary Agencies Directory 1993, NCVO Publications, 13th ed., 1993.

People Who Help, Profile Publications, 3rd ed., 1992.

Directory for Disabled People, Woodhead-Faulkner, 6th ed., 1991.

Disabled Rights Handbook, 1994–95, Disability Alliance, 1994.

Directory of Black and Ethnic Community Health Services in London, MIND, 1990.

THE HEALTH SERVICE

Health Information Line
(0800) 665544
A free information service that offers patients facts and advice about the NHS in their region, including waiting times for operations and how to complain about poor service, as well as general information on health and diseases.

Department of Health
General enquiries: Richmond House, 79 Whitehall, London SW1A 2NS, tel: (071) 210 3000.

Chief Executive of the NHS
Quarry House,
Quarry Hill, Leeds LS2 7UE

The Welsh Office
Cathays Park, Cardiff CF1 3NQ, tel: (0222) 825111

The Scottish Office
Home and Health Department, St Andrew's House, Regent Road, Edinburgh EH1 3DE, tel: (031) 556 8400

Northern Ireland Office
Department of Health and Social Services, Dundonald House, Upper Newtonards Road, Belfast BT4 3SF, tel. (0232) 650111

National Association of Health Authorities & Trusts (NAHAT)
Birmingham Research Park, Vincent Drive, Birmingham B15 2SQ, tel: (021) 471 4444
NAHAT's primary role is to express the collective views of family health services authorities, health authorities, and NHS trusts on important national issues affecting the NHS. It aims to educate and inform the public about the achievements and needs of the NHS.

Association of Community Health Councils for England and Wales (ACHCEW)
30 Drayton Park, London N5 1PB, tel: (071) 609 8405
A forum for member community health councils.

Association of Welsh Community Health Councils
13 Gelliwastad Road, Pontypridd, Mid Glamorgan CF37 2BW, tel: (0443) 405830

Association of Scottish Health Councils
5 Leamington Terrace, Edinburgh EH10 4JW, tel: (031) 229 2344

MAKING A COMPLAINT

The Health Service Commissioner for England
Church House, Great Smith Street,
London SW1P 3BW, tel: (071) 276 2035

The Health Service Commissioner for Scotland
2nd floor, 11 Melville Crescent,
Edinburgh EH3 7LU, tel: (031) 225 7465

The Health Service Commissioner for Wales
4th floor Pearl Assurance House,
Greyfriars Road, Cardiff CF1 3AG,
tel: (0222) 394621

The following organisations are responsible for registering the members of each profession. Each has a disciplinary committee that can deal with complaints relating to personal and professional misconduct of members, and can strike the practitioner off the register so that he or she can no longer practise.

Doctors
General Medical Council
44 Hallam Street, London W1N 6AE,
tel: (071) 580 7642

Dentists
General Dental Council
37 Wimpole Street, London W1M 8DQ,
tel: (071) 486 2171

Opticians
General Optical Council
41 Harley Street, London W1N 2DJ,
tel: (071) 580 3898
Complaints about *ophthalmic medical practitioners* or *ophthalmologists* should be addressed to the General Medical Council.

Complaints about *orthoptists (*who treat children's squints and other visual defects*)* should be addressed to the Orthoptists Board of the Council for Professions Supplementary to Medicine (*see below*).

Complaints about the provision of spectacles and contact lenses *not* supplied by the NHS can be taken to the *Optical Consumer Complaints Service* (PO Box 2JX, London W1A 2JX, tel: 071-261 1017). This is a negotiating body that will take up complaints by patients against practitioners. Free to the public. Their decisions are not legally binding.

Pharmacists
Royal Pharmaceutical Society of Great Britain
Law Department, 1 Lambeth High Street,
London SE1 7JN, tel: (071) 735 9141
or 36 York Place, Edinburgh EH1 3HU,
tel: (031) 556 4386
If the Society is unable to offer advice, a local inspector of the Society will contact the patient to discuss the complaint and inform him/her of the options available.

Speech therapists
College of Speech & Language Therapists
7 Bath Place, Rivington Street,
London EC2A 3DR,
tel: (071) 613 3855

Nurses, midwives and health visitors
United Kingdom Central Council for Nursing, Midwifery and Health Visiting
23 Portland Place, London W1N 3AF,
tel: (071) 637 7181

Other practitioners

The Council for Professions Supplementary to Medicine

Park House, 184 Kennington Park Road, London SE11 4BU, tel: (071) 582 0866

Patients should deal with the appropriate Board: chiropodists, physiotherapists, occupational therapists, radiographers, orthoptists, dieticians.

For medical negligence

Action for Victims of Medical Accidents (AVMA)

Bank Chambers, 1 London Road, Forest Hill, London SE23 3TP, tel: (081) 291 2793

Provides information for people who think they may have suffered a medical accident. Referral to experienced solicitors and medical experts.

HEALTH RIGHTS

College of Health

St Margaret's House, 21 Old Ford Road, London E2 1PL, tel: (081) 983 1225
Hospital waiting lists information: (081) 983 1133
Recorded information on 350 conditions: (0345) 678444 (local call rate)

The College aims to help people keep healthy, care for themselves when ill and make the best use of the NHS. It keeps a list of well over 1600 self-help groups. Information about hospital waiting lists is updated regularly and covers the UK.

Patients Association

18 Victoria Park Square, London E2 9PF, tel: (081) 981 5676/5695

Provides an independent information and advice service to individual patients and carers concerning patients rights, complaints procedures, access to health services, and appropriate self-help groups. Represents the collective interests of patients to government, health professionals and the media.

Health Rights

Unit 405, Brixton Small Business Centre, 444 Brixton Road, London SW9 8EJ, tel: (071) 274 4000 ext. 326

Set up to protect and enhance

individual and collective rights to good health, remove inequalities and discrimination within the NHS, and work for good public health policies that promote health for all. Advice and information service.

Citizens Advice Bureaux (CABx)

Over 1000 CABx throughout the country offer confidential and impartial advice over the widest possible range of subjects, including using the health services, complaining about treatment, benefits, and the law. To find your nearest bureau, look in the phone book under 'C' or the community pages of the Thomson Directory.

National Association for Patient Participation

11 Hardie Avenue, Moreton, Mersyside L46 6BJ, tel: (051) 677 9616

Promotes and supports setting up of 'patient participation groups' in GPs' surgeries and health centres, with the aim of improving services.

Consumers' Association

2 Marylebone Road, London NW1 4DF, tel: (071) 486 5544

Publishes *Which? Way to Health* and conducts research into health services and products.

BETTER HEALTH

Help for Health Trust
Highcroft Cottage, Romsey Road,
Winchester SO22 5DH,
tel: (0962) 849100
Health enquiry line: (0345) 678679
Holds a database of over 3000 self-help
groups and an extensive collection of
health information literature. Publishes
a range of patient information sheets.

Health Literature Line
Tel: (0800) 555777
Central Office of Information
freephone line that provides leaflets,
posters and other information on
government health campaigns: AIDS,
drug and solvent abuse in children,
traveller's health, women and health,
health and the elderly, the 'back to
sleep' campaign (cot death), family
planning, and the mental health and
septicaemia campaigns. Organ donor
cards can also be obtained by ringing
this number.

Women's Health
52 Featherstone Street, London EC1Y 8RT,
tel: (071) 251 6580
A national information and resource
centre for women's health.

British Heart Foundation
14 Fitzhardinge Street, London
W1H 4DH, tel: (071) 935 0185
Research into the causes, diagnosis,
treatment and prevention of heart
disease. Information service and
publications available.

BACUP (British Association of Cancer United Patients)
3 Bath Place, Rivington Street, London
EC2A 3JR, tel: (071) 696 9003
Cancer information: (071) 613 2121/
(outside London) (0800) 181199
Provides information, support and
counselling to cancer patients, families
and friends. Wide range of publications
available.

Health Education Authority (HEA)
Hamilton House, Mabledon Place, London
WC1H 9TX, tel: (071) 383 3833
Provides information and advice about
health directly to members of the
public through publications, videos
and other services.

Royal Society for the Promotion of Health
RSH House, 38A St George's Drive, London
SW1V 4BH, tel: (071) 630 0121
Concerned with most aspects of
disease prevention and health
promotion. Worldwide multi-
disciplinary membership.

LIFE SAVING

British Red Cross Society
9 Grosvenor Crescent, London SW1X 7EJ,
tel: (071) 235 5454
Over 85,000 volunteers work across
the country providing first aid and
emergency services to those most in
need in their local communities. The
Society also runs training courses in first
aid, nursing and social work.

St John Ambulance
1 Grosvenor Crescent, London
SW1X 7EF, tel: (071) 235 5231
Organises courses in first aid. Volunteer
members provide first-aid cover at
public events and carry out welfare
work for the sick, disabled and lonely.

Medic Alert Foundation
12 Bridge Wharf, 156 Caledonian Road,
London N1 9UU, tel: (071) 833 3034
Provides complete emergency
identification and information service
for individuals with specific medical
conditions or allergies.

Organ donation
Organ donor cards are available
through doctors' surgeries, post offices,
libraries and other public places. They
may also be obtained by phoning free
on (0800) 555777.

Blood transfusion
For information on the blood
transfusion service and the location of
your nearest centre, ring (0345) 711711
(local call rates).

MENTAL HEALTH

MIND (National Association for Mental Health)
Granta House, 15–19 Broadway,
Stratford, London E15 4BQ,
tel: (081) 519 2122
Information line: (081) 522 1728
Campaigns for improvements in mental
health services through over 200 local
associations. Publishes guides and reports.

Scottish Association for Mental Health
Atlantic House, 38 Gardner's Crescent,
Edinburgh EH3 8DQ, tel: (031) 229 9687
Information on mental health and illness

Northern Ireland Association for Mental Health
80 University Street, Belfast BT7 1HE,
tel: (0232) 328474
Information on all aspects of
mental health.

Mental Health Foundation
37 Mortimer Street, London W1N 7RJ,
tel: (071) 580 0145
Promotes and finances innovative
community care projects in the field of
mental health, and research into mental
disorders of every kind.

LEARNING DIFFICULTIES

Mencap (Royal Society for Mentally Handicapped Children and Adults)
123 Golden Lane, London EC1Y 0RT, tel: (071) 454 0454
Offers support, information and advice to people with learning difficulties and their families through over 500 local societies.

Enable (Scottish Society for the Mentally Handicapped)
13 Elmbank Street, Glasgow G2 4QA, tel: (041) 226 4541
Concerned with the needs and rights of people with learning difficulties.

People First
207 King's Cross Road, London WC1X 9DB, tel: (071) 713 6400
An independent self-advisory organisation, run by people with learning difficulties, which encourages members to learn to take responsibility and speak up for themselves.

Values into Action
Oxford House, Derbyshire Street, London E2 6HG, tel: (071) 729 5436
Works for the rights of people with learning difficulties, and to ensure that they participate in decisions that affect their lives.

National Citizen Advocacy
2 St Paul's Road, London N1 2QR
An umbrella organisation for local groups of people who befriend and support disadvantaged or isolated people living in institutions or in the community, in order to help them express their wishes and exercise their rights.

British Institute of Learning Disabilities
Wolverhampton Road, Kidderminster, Worcs. DY10 3PP, tel: (0562) 850251
Aims to raise the standards of treatment, care and management of people with learning disabilities, both in hospital and in the community.

Rescare
Rayner House, 23 Higher Hillgate, Stockport, Cheshire SK1 3ER, tel: (061) 474 7323
Seeks to promote the welfare of people with learning difficulties in all types of residential care – hospital or community based or at home. It is dedicated to seeking a range of care provisions, including sheltered village communities.

DISABILITY

British Council of Organisations of Disabled People (BCOD)
De Bradelei House, Chapel Street, Belper, Derbys. DE56 1AR, tel: (0773) 828182
Acts as an umbrella for the growing number of groups of people with disabilities.

Disability Alliance
1st floor east, Universal House, 88–94 Wentworth Street, London E1 7SA,
tel: (071) 247 8776
Advice line: (071) 247 8763
Campaigns for improvements in the rights and services of people with disabilities. Research arm provides benefits advice service by phone or letter, and publishes the *Disability Rights Handbook*.

DIAL UK
Park Lodge, St Catherine's Hospital, Tickhill Road, Balby, Doncaster, South Yorks. DN4 8QN, tel: (0302) 310123
DIAL stands for Disablement Information and Advice Lines – a network of centres throughout the country giving information, advice and practical assistance to disabled people.

Contact a Family
4th floor, 170 Tottenham Court Road, London W1P 0HA, tel: (071) 222 2695
Publishes the *Directory of Specific Conditions and Rare Syndromes in Children* and, through self-help groups, links up families of children with special needs.

In Touch
10 Norman Road, Sale, Cheshire M33 3DF, tel: (061) 905 2440
Provides information and contacts for parents of children with special needs and rare disorders.

Disabled Living Foundation
380/384 Harrow Road, London W9 2HU, tel: (071) 289 6111
Gives advice and information by telephone and letter on daily problems affecting people with disabilities, including incontinence, clothing, footwear and household equipment and aids.

Royal Association for Disability and Rehabilitation (RADAR)
12 City Forum, 250 City Road, London EC1V 8AF, tel: (071) 250 3222
Particularly concerned with access, education, employment, mobility and leisure.

The following regional organisations provide an information service on all aspects of disability and local disability groups.

Wales Council for the Disabled
Llys Ifor, Crescent Road, Caerphilly, Mid Glamorgan CF8 1XL

Disability Scotland
Princes House, 5 Shandwick Place, Edinburgh EH2 4RG, tel: (031) 229 8632

Disability Action
2 Annadale Avenue, Belfast BT7 3UR, tel: (0232) 491011

The Prince of Wales' Advisory Group on Disability
8 Bedford Row, London WC1R 4BA, tel: (071) 430 0558/9
Works to improve the quality of life of people with disabilities.

PREGNANCY AND CHILDBIRTH

Family Planning Association
27/35 Mortimer Street, London
W1N 7RJ, tel: (071) 636 7866
Provides a nationwide family planning
information service as well as help with
questions about sexuality and
reproductive health. Free catalogue of
books and leaflets available.

Brook Advisory Centres
Central Office, 153a East Street, London
SE17 2SD, tel: (071) 708 1234
Centres in Edinburgh, Birmingham,
Bristol, Burnley, Coventry, Liverpool,
London, Milton Keynes, Salford and
Telford provide contraception,
pregnancy tests, counselling.

British Pregnancy
Advisory Service
Austy Manor, Wootton Wawen, Solihull,
West Midlands B95 6BX, tel: (0564)
793225
25 local branches throughout Britain
offer pregnancy testing, contraception,
counselling and information about
pregnancy, sterilisation and abortion.

National Childbirth Trust
Alexandra House, Oldham Terrace,
London W3 6NH, tel: (081) 992 8637
Information and support in pregnancy,
childbirth and early parenthood. Over
350 branches in the UK.

Association for Improvements in
the Maternity Services (AIMS)
40 Kingswood Avenue, London
NW6 6LS, tel: (081) 960 5585
Offers information, support and advice
to parents about all aspects of maternity
care, including parents' rights, the
choices available and complaints
procedures. Send a SAE for free
publications list.

Maternity and Health Links
The Old Co-op, 38-42 Chelsea Road,
Easton, Bristol BS5 6AF,
tel: (0272) 558495
Linkworkers act as advocates and
befrienders of non-English-speaking
mothers and other Asian patients
(including Chinese)who have difficulty
in receiving care from the NHS. The
organisation also works to make the
health service more aware of the needs
of such patients.

OTHER USEFUL ORGANISATIONS

Action for Sick Children
Argyle House, 29–31 Euston Road,
London NW1 2SD, tel: (071) 833 2041
Joins patients and professionals in
improving the standards and quality of
care for all children in hospital.

Hospice Information Service
St Christopher's Hospice, 51–59 Lawrie
Road, London SE26 6DZ,
tel: (081) 778 9252
Telephone and written enquiries
welcomed on all aspects of hospice
provision. Publish the free *Directory of
Hospice Services* (send 11"×9" SAE with
52p stamps) and maintain a list of
overseas contacts.

**Churches' Council for Health and
Healing (CCHH)**
St Marylebone Parish Church,
Marylebone Road, London NW1 5LT,
tel: (071) 935 6374
CCHH's 'Medical Forum' provides a
meeting ground for doctors, ministers
of religion, nurses and others by means
of local discussion groups, publications
and conferences.

Published in 1993 by
Channel 4 Television
60 Charlotte Street
London W1P 2AX
New edition 1994

Produced by
Broadcasting Support Services

Writer: Robert Eagle
Editor: Derek Jones
Editorial consultant: Nancy Duin
Designer: Wave Design Ltd, Hastings
Printer: Adept Print
Distributed by Broadcasting Support
Services

Broadcasting Support Services is an
educational charity, which runs
helplines and provides follow-up
services for viewers and listeners.

For further copies, please send a
cheque or postal order for £2.00
(made payable to Channel 4
Television) to:

CHANNEL FOUR TELEVISION

TODAY'S NHS
PO Box 4000
London W3 6XJ or Cardiff CF5 2XT